A FIELD GUIDE TO THE REHEARSAL

A FIELD GUIDE
TO THE REHEARSAL

DENNIS BARONE

BLAZEVOX[BOOKS]
Buffalo, New York

A Field Guide to the Rehearsal
by Dennis Barone
Copyright © 2022

Published by BlazeVOX [books]

Printed in the United States of America

Interior design and typesetting by Geoffrey Gatza
Cover Art: Vincent Baldassano, Chapels & Temples #5, acrylic on linen, 2015.

First Edition
ISBN: 978-1-60964-397-3
Library of Congress Control Number: 2021952026

BlazeVOX [books]
131 Euclid Ave
Kenmore, NY 14217
Editor@blazevox.org

publisher of weird little books

BlazeVOX [books]

blazevox.org

21 20 19 18 17 16 15 14 13 12 01 02 03 04 05 06 07 08 09 10 11

BlazeVOX

Acknowledgements

Some of this work appeared in *Atlas and Alice, Blue Moon, Circumference, The Cold Spring Journal, Noon, Ovunque Siamo, The Paterson Literary Review, Posit, Raritan, Shot Glass Journal,* and *Voices in Italian Americana.* "Fortunes" appeared in *The Prose Poem* and in the chapbook *The Disguise of Events* (Quale Press).

I completed the writings in section II with support from the Connecticut Office of the Arts, which also receives funding from the National Endowment for the Arts, a federal agency.

Contents

For Debbie

A Field Guide
to the Rehearsal

Off-Balance

It is a narcotic, the acting line. Consider the actor's notebook: its contemporized antiquity; its automated egoism. The actor's children have two arms and two legs but are scolded by those with pointed stinger, and by tusk they have been shoved off school grounds. The actor's rage carries all the import of an unravelling past and a quickening plot. On the boards, phones are denied. We read about a certain originality of expression, peppered with political debate. *The New York Times* offers an occasional column. The actor learns to sing and dance as well as to act. All this trouble and still no change – another ambulance passes in the night. Thy will be done, the actor prays, before ordering wine. Consider the hotels actors occupy. Act three had come to an end in violent storm, trees shaking. A sanctuary of one sort or another would be called for – a place to ice old wounds, belly-up to the bar and order drinks all around, a pianist off to one side plunking out old show tunes. The bucket brigade stumbles down the steep stairs locked arm-in-arm singing, "There's a hole in the bucket. Go mend it!" Such times as these cannot be easily forgotten. The company's official photographer snaps an impromptu photo of the boisterous gathering. Next consider the element of surprise in a stage production, that unexpected turn that comes in the final twenty minutes, and what a time the audience has of it, guessing, anticipating how the merry couple will meet their inexorable fate -- grace or shame, tragedy or comedy. An actor must be a ballerina, prepared to rise on toe one moment and decline as the dead swan in the next act and to do so with good cheer and that sort of professionalism union rules require. Trust us, we know. We have been there on-stage for the premiere of *The Return of the Soldier.* When the audience clapped, we bowed for the better part of an hour.

Happy Starry Night

The practitioner hurries past. She does not see me in the wall. Two guests walk by the place I find myself wedged, and I try to make eye-contact. My mouth will not move so words of solicitation are impossible. The specialists consult one another. They are quite serious, but their aims seem ludicrous to me. What is the purpose? They'll cut and they'll chop. Others will seek similar degrees, their nest, and maintain order until an end of sorts, and then the circle-spring draws taut again and more moments click away, heels down the hallway ever-busy. Is there a point of return so low that effort is pointless or must the attempt be made despite the fears and the chills and the wails of the one who has little say in the matter? And even if the forms have been signed, the ethical-professional agreement, might the specialists go ahead and flip it for a time? The wall provides some objective distance from the body in the bed, the body that gets wheeled off, returned nearly a day later, not quite good as new. First, the man in the wall and the one in the bed rejoin. Then there is an act of kindness and he cries in thanks. Then he thinks of some things he must do, some pieces that he must put next to other ones in order to make something. This is the purpose, the rush. He returns to his immersion in the community of others.

Oath

There is an old road that holds earth and stones -- persons like-minded. They are bound to that conformity more or less achieved by inheritance. They are not to be elevated to historic good sense and righteousness. It takes ages for them to be translated in the most formal courts: our purpose here to test and gauge facts. The facts supersede malice and other ties that somewhat fatalistically resort to dangers of sharp contrast. It is notorious and seriously contemplated in this regard how dangerous it will be to keep constantly in mind unwritten principles of our own. What forces must dwell between consent and the sacred inescapable world. What is important here is the grouping of elements that line up against the system itself. The various states compelled to function in regard to moral principles warp all variations of unwritten laws. If it is pointed out that people are wholly and intimately trembling upon the abyss, why entrust a frank and earnest appeal to that terrible heritage? Let us go and detect language. Is it not strange to dispute? It is unfair to hesitate to petition. What stimuli faces us and no other population? The very machinery deeply and justly cherished by these shores? Our present vision is an argument justified to these ends. We take, not perish.

The Wild Animal-Breath of the World

When I came home from the hospital, I could not get comfortable in any position – standing, sitting, or reclining. And because of this I could not sleep for several weeks. The health-care industry offers many remedies and we tried them all. Some were suggested by friends or relatives and others by sales staff at the medical supply store or pharmacy. Everyone who stopped by to visit brought a thousand-page book and several bars of chocolate. They also brought their advice. I listened to their thoughts and considered carefully all they suggested. But for the life of me I could not understand why they believed someone recovering from illness needed to read a novel that could barely be lifted, and the curative powers of chocolate must be a myth. All that the chocolate would do would be to make me fat and keep me up at night and, as I said, I already had a serious problem trying to sleep. Several of our friends suggested the same solution for the insomnia: the cube pillow. Magic it was not. Immediately upon hearing the suggestion, my wife went and bought one at Charm Medical. I do not know how much she paid and I probably do not want to know. Once while attending a conference in New York – at the Institute – we stayed at the Bryant Park Hotel. I like Bryant Park a lot. I like the new Bank of America tower that is right across the street. But there was something odd about the hotel. Too much red in the décor and when we had a cocktail at the bar, the leather outfits of the staff surprised if not shocked us. In our room there was an advertising booklet for sex toys where one might expect to find a Bible or a room service menu. One of the items listed in this catalogue: the cube pillow designed to aid the felicity of one's partner in reaching zones difficult of access. I did not know if the pillow purchased at Charm matched that offered in New York, but I did know that after nine days and nine nights of being poked, drained, sawed, and sewn, sensuality of any sort did not drive me wild; rather, discomfort did, and the cube pillow offered no solace; only a new and different sort of discombobulation. Into the closet it went, virtually unused but non-returnable. And my stomach and chest broke out in a bright red rash. My skin started to peel as if I had sunburn from a holiday at the beach. One prescribed ointment stopped the skin from dropping off my torso, but turned my tummy and pectorals an even brighter red. Apply a cold compress, we were advised. We did so and the redness lightened. Then a nurse applied a product named Detach-It to the derma-bond that nearly covered me. This is a product, I am sure, available at either medical supply or hardware store. A rectangle of thick glue came off easily but left a mess all over the examination room floor. I apologized. The nurse said not to worry. She would sweep it up. What had become of me, I wondered? Of course, by this time another nine nights had passed. Time cures all wounds. It was good to be home. The rash had dissipated. My appetite had returned. I slipped into a comfortable complacency and took a very long nap.

Resolved

Not any song will do. Not all the composers' works. Not the notes contained, boxed-sets. Not the longest solo nor the final bow. It won't work: fill the bar, the staff. Just a few words might do. Just these words, you know, that end with you, but mumbled like any jumble of indifferent sound.

The Orb of Prague

It is true that on the evening of Monday the twentieth my initial reaction had been one of total disbelief. We still had the dim light of Indian summer and what I thought was another reason for short, dark days. The bronze-age began that morning, a morning that made faces visible to words: dry words, dead words. Ask him to hear some other sound – a pelican too grim for salvation and those problems without dollars. Rain fell with bits of sky, a weather that felt like disaster. Rain begged too many questions. An afternoon apart and then something after little drops. When I stood there that Monday, off in a giggle, the most terrible things came back to the hapless author. A child in New Haven had ignored eternity. Such thoughtlessness surprised me and the clouds expanded and darkened. Each of us slept in his cloak. For once we could not find wherewithal to employ our pencils. We refused to leave the house: its old bricks bear the marks of fingers that shaped them. The sound of the wind through our masks became an anthem. And when we found him that Monday, he did his chin-ups on the edge of the crater, a glass object by his side. This, he said, becomes the light, the quiet, the sound of birds. I do not want to repeat the catastrophe of last year: an unpleasant scene in the town square, followed by a walk without direction. The heart will never give up this promise of truth. Even wilderness makes light a kingdom.

First Light of Day

Branches sway and break in the storm. Trees seem to cry out as if given voice, as if people once known; now, gone. Here soldiers fell and these trees grew from decaying bone. Young men fired rifles through the windblown snow. In the storm, white ground reddened. I took out my sketchpad, drew what I saw, survived, made a print of it, framed it so that you can see it where you stand this morning warm, comforted, free from any storm.

Hawaiian Shirt

I will go eye to eye with the shark, tie my board to the trunk of a palm, and battle swirling eddies until moonrise. This is something I can use, something better than chocolate logs and thousand-page novels. The turtle has its shell; I have my shirt, and we both survive, head-up, and medium sized with a flowery border all along the sides. And we swim to the beach, bask in the sun, day-dream a little, and imagine returning next year to tell the story of how we survived. I sliced that shark in two with an especially sharp button. The turtle swam out to sea and waited for the coconuts to drop.

Clothes Come Out of the Wash

Let's get a cat that sleeps all day. Let's play more, talk less; go to the movies and all-night bars; learn stars, forget sun – heat of day. Street life! Nightlife! Begin life! Life like a chemist's crucible with small amounts of phosphorous light and sulfuric soot. Street life spark Ammino Ammonio to equality organic life. Electric us! Great city into your warm dirty sheets. We sweat with your forever river buildings in praise of Walt Whitman Shopping Center.

He will become breathless; return home, but skip the stairs and ride the elevator. It begins. He will travel in the quiet caboose to the room of testing and waiting and an expert's opinion turned quickly to detested fact. Ushered off to the top floor, a swan will maintain order and notify others of things as they should be or their alteration. He will be offered a two-day reprieve from the beast and its feathery touch. He will accept and on tender-hooks watch an episode on TV. The next morning, he will be greeted by the kindest of men, a man of many anecdotes, and then he will return to sleep. After six or so forgotten hours, he will awake to the concerned voices of friends and relatives. That swan will scare them, as it would anyone, and then there are also so many wires with faint possibility of becoming epic lines in some future revision. He will sit and then he will walk. He will climb the stairs. He will walk the short path with the kind woman of boastful voice, not realizing each turn costs half a thousand. He will do this for three days and three nights, sometimes on his own while others sleep. He will feel a bit revived. He will look at his hands and feet and he will not recognize them. This, too, will be explained. He will wheel to the basement and have a liter drained as all the people gathered in the room talk of Boston and he will try not to complain. They will say, do you want to see? And he will say, no, thanks, but no. He will await departure. First, one day they'll say, and then the next, and there will be a threat of a longer stay, but, no, it'll be that next one as someone had promised, perhaps the director of it all. And he will depart, saying goodbye to the experts and to his former student who had graduated and then joined their team. He will have questions such as why such ceaseless chills and should he eat a banana? And he will think, but, surely, they can wait until another day.

Hold Still

That any eye may see it: the drift of a ship mid-sea or line. And what comes up from the ground this time of year: anticipated, but not yet green.

Michelangelo's David

"What a misfortune it is to be made as I am made," Malaparte wrote. There is nothing wrong with my heart. It keeps its regular beat better than any metronome, finer than the finest perpetual motion machines from the courts of baroque kings and queens. "It is just one of those things": an explanation that fails to instill confidence in the listener regarding the intelligence of the diagnostician. But we go with the suggested remedy; nod yes, proceed. The little boy drops his Popsicle stick in the water, rushes to the other side of the bridge, and watches it float downstream, farther and farther away from where he stands.

Three pages. Now counting. A shopping-list. A to do list. Too many for that. Think of the mat alongside the frame, the crosswalk, or something hung on the refrigerator. A full roll of paper towel, no printed design applied. Agnes Martin very early in the morning. Wallace Stevens in winter. A coffee-mug with no coffee; a tea-cup with no tea. Something sanitized before surgery. A thick book looked at from the side, someone's autobiography. Fog – when the car lights hit it just so (now we're moving). Robert Irwin alone in his room. Someone's eyes closed, ready for yoga-practice or prayer. Morris's empty loom. Carrara or "oh, moon," etc. Fifty-year old appliances: still working. Lampshades or drum-skins. The dots of polka-dots. A lightbulb lit. A voice speaking and the listener not yet ready to hear it, to heed its beckoning call in the forest and then a meeting with the speaking tiger. Of necessity, following instructions precisely. The tiger growled but expressed kindness and humility. He listened to the tiger; observed the ripples of its stripes as it spoke. The tiger especially liked the tulip garden and wanted to walk there, all the bright colors of the blooms. Then the next day the tiger woke early: all across the morning sky stretched himself until the brightness of noon negated all trace of animal presence. The hours advanced despite the fact that someone had turned all clocks toward the wall, as if this might slow down or even stall for some moments the onward progression of hours. The moon came up, beckoning the return. Shadows now across the field, two scarecrows and the hum of distant tractors. One shadow aspires, seeks, wants, sees, and so speaks to the scarecrows. They appear not to be actively listening. They watch and wait for the mailman. Sometimes they count backwards: three-two-one. They are impatient; also, immovable. The scarecrows and the shadows lift their faces to the moonlight, take it all into their bodies. The branches of the leafless tree. The roof of the house next door. Part of a telephone pole. Part of a window. Breathing and cancellation. Clean-up. Put away. Check list. Tie shoes. Millions of facts in the night of knowledge. We have a picture of such far away stillness, a bend in the light. At the edge of a stream, something recalled for a moment. Someone starts to speak but only stutters a syllable or two and then stops, looks down at the ground, ashamed. And then a melody: oboe concerto (Bellini). Barely heard but loud enough to lift up, to perk up, to listen, and to find that listening pleasant, worthwhile, and a reason to walk closer to the sound, in its direction which seems to be coming from the nearest town, a small ornamented lyceum built a century before, built when the composer lived, a building built in this small town for just this purpose, for music and its appreciation. One doesn't often think of the oboe, but here, now, it offered many reasons for joy – each note another one. The horses lifted their heads. The sheep and the cows. The swan stayed quiet for once and ceased its honking. Bellini, the opera composer, had written a concerto. All around the fence creatures gathered to listen. When it stopped, the people clapped, the animals bent their heads down to the trough. The walker returned to the creek and recalled the sound, the notes until he could no longer do so. He thought of a kitchen decorated in white tile and black wood. He grew hungry and his stomach growled, but there was nothing to eat. The moon rose and he put his hands in the water.

The Ark-Car

Once it rained so hard that after reaching your car in the lot you thought about going back inside and high up in the office tower where you worked, much higher than the floor on which you worked. You thought the water would soon reach the car windows and then the windows of your third-floor office and soon after even the rooftop helipad. That's how hard the rain fell. But you also wanted to get home. You started the car and left the lot. Already the Pig River swelled its banks and flooded Boulevard. You went a block beyond and tried another street. People honked their horns. You slid through the center between lanes. More people honked their horns. It was slow going, and you were late and cold and wet upon arrival. You entered through the side door by the garage; marched right past a platter of steaming hot food; and got two pair of shoes, two pair of socks, two pair of gloves, two hats, and two umbrellas; paused a moment by the door, and said, "For the car." And the thunder drew near. And rain continued to fall and to fall and to fall.

Day by Day

Those dreamt lines should come back to me. Those are better than the dream of the four-part division. One after another it seems they are in quick succession until morning, that first or second birds' call outside the window where the branches, so lush with green now, appear almost ready to break the glass.

Paul walks with a cane now. There wasn't much I could say when I ran past him this morning, for I did not know if the afternoon reception had been planned as a surprise event. Then, too, I didn't want to lie. "How are you?" "Fine, fine." "Why you're looking great!" "Not really." "What do you mean?" Etc. You see. It used to be called Prospect Hill, but they took part of the name out. Taking things out. Yes. I know.

Once more I forgot my opening lines. Oh, well. Wouldn't it have been nice to hear about Rio instead of the humorous anesthesiologist and parti-colored surgical caps? And today the choices are between oils, pastels, or prints. Ice-cream first; followed by an examination of the aesthetic kind. Why do some say "awesome" when clearly what they refer to may be described as ordinary? They have refused to read Burke, or Longinus, *On the Sublime.* I will carry *Paradise* in with me this time convinced, as I am, that Canto XXX holds the key to Stevens's late poem "The River of Rivers in Connecticut." This requires more time.

Psalm 118:24 – This is the day the Lord has made. We will rejoice and be glad in it. This day and all the days before us filled with light and air; filled with ricotta for the cannoli on the table, a round table that occasionally wobbles and that is made out of distressed wood.

They say: when it rains it pours. I say: look out for more (of me). I followed the same path, the same circular route as the day before and as the day before that and tomorrow – yet once again down Fern back on Asylum and et cetera. This repetition is not purgatory; it is – for now, for here – paradise. Remember that this time one year ago we had spent a hot afternoon climbing the stairs up to the top of the Duomo. Quiet a view. At some point in time, however, every tourist, every pilgrim and penitent must descend.

A Venetian calm may be just what the dining room requires. Its atmospheric mist and pink tones would add to the tranquility of the nearby blue and green. And a basket encircled by red, a basket holding magazines, cleaned-out once or twice per year. Guests might browse through an issue of *Connecticut Explored* surprised to find that the Albers lived in a typical suburban raised-ranch tract house. Here they lived their atypical lives.

"Purveyor of life," Sandeep Jauhar has written, "the heart is also its Grim Reaper." An obvious place for some sort of ending, but we must go back up the mountain to the other side where the river flows with water sweet as honey.

After we hang the Venetian scene by Henry Cooke White who also lived on this street, I will say, looks good, and I will look at the image and discover there, two people I know walking by the Doge's Palace, my niece and her husband. How can this be? In New Mexico we saw the people line-up at the sacred site awaiting their chance at a miracle. We saw the spiral staircase that according to engineering science should not stand.

And here in this chair, feet firmly resting upon the floor, I look out the window in the direction of the birdsong and recall the hawk that sat upon the fence a week before and looked as if all traffic would be directed by his wing.

So, he said to me, this sort can rarely be genetic and usually can be traced to environmental factors and I said, so that explains it, I grew up in New Jersey. Chuckled then. And how many weeks ago was that conversation?

Take the words from the dictionary and carry them with you in circumstances pleasing or depressing. Remember how Pascal D'Angelo suffered in an ice storm.

One revolves slowly and refers to another realm. It represents the lyrical. The response so burdened becomes impossible. Good-bye to transformation and undeniable markings.

And after there would be a parade, but the new design for the town common had not yet been completed. The hardware store had permanently closed and the building become "available." The bakery opened early. It had expanded into the space next door. The Congregational church displayed the date 1852 in large gold numbers. Up a slight incline a late nineteenth-century Italianate villa had been painted yellow some years ago. It needs repainting, and the cupola blew off in the October storm.

Put either foot forward when ready to begin. Count the days, but not the steps taken in each of those days. The old dirt path will be paved and even the carpenter will find his walkway changed into a driveway. Should the Dutch scenes be saved, then we must consider where to hang them? The man near the bridge cannot find his dog and sadness overwhelms him. The doors of the church open slightly and he can hear the singing from inside. His spirits lift for some moments.

Here the river has been contained in pipes buried below ground. The engineer, on occasion, reaches in and moves things around a bit so that they are certain to move along. The engineer contemplates paragraphs in spring, a rise of elevation necessary for the continued maintenance of all required parts. Let's hear what he has to say before we make our judgment, our own estimate of the facts.

Later we might return to the scene with clearer vision, we might move north to south. Gone fishing – the sign left at the door or this one somewhat similar but of no relation, "Wise men fish here." Yes, that location had been well-stocked. Now, long abandoned.

What to sell, what to save, what to store: these are the decisions to be made. And the documents, all of them must be photocopied for the paperless office.

The news has not been inspiring. There are too many parts and each one has been predetermined to fail at some point. The analyst's task is to estimate the time and place of breakdown and prepare each person for the inevitable. The analyst gives one many questions to answer. In this way, each person remains busy and does not become distressed. The program may succeed (even if the person does not).

An advanced model increases the number by one. In so doing, a flame continues to lean in one direction but does not diminish or fade. The crow stands nearby on its green rock and nods with approval all day and all night.

On Sundays we rest. We eat our muffins and drink our coffee. Sometimes the paper arrives before we're up; sometimes we must wait for it. The oldest continuously published newspaper begins to look like the smallest newspaper in America.

He rose and walked round the hall not once as suggested, but three times. This stroll sent him home where he called the objects on the shelves, the images on the walls – talismans. Gladly, he would follow his assigned regimen. If anything, restraint became necessary less he push off toward some distant coast or sprint to the summit of our state's highest place and when atop sing non-stop sacred spirituals Gospel hymns of unending joy.

To record the thoughts of idle reverie -- and worry. To move out of the past and into the present and on to the future. The fiercest agonies have the shortest reign. Those are the words of the poet who in Turin attended a church service such as could not be shared on Long Island.

But these matters offer only momentary disguise for the real matter at hand. Should the laying-on of hands be tried? In New Mexico miracles worked each morning. In the dusty yard before the sanctuary were cast off crutches, abandoned braces, and even one glass eye thought at first to be a child's lost marble.

Wait for tomorrow. You will go to sleep and then it'll seem you merely blinked your eyes and you'll wake up and it'll be over. First, two feet will wiggle once again and then animation will work its way up from there. In the mind, a mountain may be climbed; a race, run. In the mind, a government might cancel your permit; refuse to allow your expedition. Back in the city square, chest players will take their contest seriously, remain oblivious to musicians as moves and countermoves play out. How much might bystanders gamble on one player or another? How long must they wait for the results?

Our view out the window looks north. We see a reflection in the window of people walking past, an almost constant stream of them. Everyone very busy. There are options, different ways to get from here to home. Those with blue gloves do not direct traffic. The canopy does not keep out all the rain. Quiet now – awaiting their beef broth or carrots and meat loaf. A word or two and then a pause. Even a ballpoint pen feels heavy. Dim the lights to protect the eyes. Things keep rolling. Here comes the Jell-O cart. In China two Canadian citizens have been detained. Blue wrap around tall buildings. Some wear a blue belt as they walk down the hall to return today's newspaper to the lounge. Look at the headlines. Someone got it. They ate everything. Nothing remains.

I have been crucified with Christ. My arms pulled back and flesh severed and the bones broken. My feet swollen and lungs filled with fluid. My groin severed and my abdomen sliced. Always a level of pain controlled and tolerable because absorbed by those who came before me. And what will be our task?

Our professor told us for the final project in his class to look to the future. What does that mean, we asked? He said, I'm not sure. And after a pause: but try it. And, so we did, but as we were doing so and making notes on our predictions and visions our pen ran out of ink. Now what do we do, we wondered? And our semester had ended, our professor had left for Italy. One of us said that it didn't really matter. We had seen the future and did not care for it. Now hold on a second, another member of our class interrupted. I like what I saw very much, thank you. The future will be wonderful. What I want to do, the classmate continued, is to tell others what we have seen, the marvels to come. And a third doubted the efficacy of such prophecy. This member asserted, no one will believe you. The people have eyes but do not see. The people have ears but will not listen to you. The people have tongues with which they will hurl darts of slander at you. You should sit on the balcony, they said.

And then the sun came out. People crossed the street, they moved along to wherever they meant to go. A man in a uniform took off his hat, and he held it in his hands close to his heart. A man with an umbrella used it to steady himself as he crossed the street, slowly, to the other side.

The park -- from the western loop to the eastern overlook (believe in something -- science, Moses – something). Tennis courts, baseball fields, a gray heron in the pond, dahlias tall, Ana Grace Marquez-Greene Playground (the Spirit blows where it will). And then home again via the woodchip trail. The tallest redwood in Connecticut. The oldest house on the block (1845) later expanded and absorbed in that expansion (1873). Tiger lilies in bloom along the drive. "When people come together in reconciliation and forgiveness, one can be sure it is the work of the Divine spirit." That's what Father Joe said.

What's it all for? Here I am standing around freezing
In this over air-conditioned room, a black band on my arm
While you lie now so still, slumber even, hardly breathing.
I, too, saw a light that came and that's now receding
Into some dark station, some zone far beyond an old barn.

What's it for? Here I am twiddling my thumbs, freezing.
"Christ Died For Our Sins": white letters fading against a red
wall;
A structure leans each ephemeral year closer to the hay-brown
lawn
While you lie now so still, slumber even hardly breathing.

Who was it that painted such over-sized, bold lettering,
Visible from every tidy corner of this suburbanized farm?
"Christ Died For Our Sins." What's it all for anyway?
I stand around dumb, freezing. All these houses, boxes really,
Built to hide all this dying. A nameless soul painted those

Words, a borrowed charm maybe. And now you lie so still,
Slumber even: breathing? There are no horses, no fields, and
No flowers, not anymore. Those old red structures are,
Usher-like, pointless, incessantly tossed into the tarn.

What's it all for? Here I am standing around freezing
While you lie now so still, slumber even, hardly breathing.

He goes down to the pool and paints children and their parents; he
paints floats in the shape of turtles and television monsters; he paints
the bright colors of an inflatable beach ball. Back upstairs we try a
tropical iced tea and he recalls early years in Maine. He asks us about
the Whites, who for some time lived in the large Queen Anne style
house up the block before moving to Waterford. We tell him we used
to live in the carriage house there and how cozy we found it. He asks
who lived in the main house at that time. And we say an orthodontist
and his family. He seems somehow saddened by the fact, oh, yes, he
says. I can see a connection, a heritage. Work done by hand with tools
and what difference brushes or drills. But we understand. Three
generations of painters, a calling forth of the beautiful versus something
much more practical: the call of career, job, money, income, and
material doo-dads. He asks us, and what of the spirit? Is the point

something more than food and shelter? We say we have not a clue and think that from his present perspective he might better inform us.

Nothing extraordinary, just the usual basic metabolic and CBC panel. I'll have to be driven and then when I get there, hope that a usable vein can be found and stuck without too much discomfort. I may return to my normal lifestyle with moderation in three weeks. Continue taking these medications ... One wonders why the vein on the left-hand has become slightly enlarged and sensitive to the slightest pressure. One wonders if there might be any connection between a tumor on a heart-valve and a tumor on a kidney (lower pole right-side). One wonders how a kidney functions if it has been reduced and sutured. One wonders, what exactly does the surgeon do during a robotic procedure? (The east coast is like a pinball machine.)

This month. This scene. These slices of peach. These sounds. And the aroma of lilac, the hotel patio that explains it. Count the days before, the days after. This paragraph. This vision. These decisions. And each one has been pre-determined, the travel difficult. Give in one direction, you see the price. This drive in the car. This turn. These years. These physicians. And another one from Primrose Hill, the images on the walls. Say I can, the tranquility of blue. This tourist. This day and every day. These shirts. These familiar sounds. And in the drawer of a desk, the sign. Gone fishing, gone to see. This I picked up and this I moved. These doors. These old barns. And I suppose on occasion an outline offered. Take the machine, the show. This yesterday and those trees, those flowers; orange ones in a red pot and yellow ones in a blue one. Give instructions, the frame. This view, out the window. This longest day. Those temperatures that rise. Those highways. And this balm, the reward gained. See the parade, the matinee. This production. This jitterbug. Those sixteen miles. And these remains. And I don't recall having fallen asleep, the afternoon. Start the music, we will drive. This bright sunlight. This better.

You go to sleep and in a blink wake-up and it'll all be over. In the east the sun rises. Sitting on a bench its rays strike you, and you try to remember. Was I awake, you ask? Recall wheels of the cart turning on the hard surface and someone saying here's a small bump and then the elevator to a room that overlooked both the original building (the oldest building) and the newest one, though there wasn't much opportunity to stand by the window and look around. What you did see appeared bowl-like, edges of green that sloped down to a contained urban space crisscrossed by streets.

On the bench, Sunday paper in hand, sunlight warms my face. It doesn't matter what's in the news or what stories the body's skin reveals. These rays and their warmth feel good; yes, they brighten up this day. I can smell coffee (not roses). I will shower. I will walk, read, and write. I will live. I will rise again tomorrow: sun up over the Travelers Tower (1906, Donn Barber). I like this building and this day and all the days to follow. I will run again and see other buildings, too, those celestial towers also tapered but unimaginable.

Focus on what is real, not what you imagine (the fracture of self-help).

      remove *m* from them and
get the
(don't move,
   don't breathe)
breath
collection of phrases and
successive positions of I
sun wheel night to
understand

become rain or mist
become white of white sheets
passion always
to behold its object
needs a perfect unit
bringing this

into equilibrium
with the world
be its I engaged

In the waiting room I read a book called *A Death of One's Own*. It said that most of all the spouse must not forget. I jotted some notes then about the Verrazano Bridge but soon realized I had forgotten what body of water it goes across. I chuckled a little bit and then it was my turn to enter.

And John Adams had claimed of this day, "the most memorable," but no one remembers and dates get confused, an erroneous one credited for the birth of this nation. And within the body politic an illness spreads that no surgery can resection and then suture with success for tomorrow and all the days to follow in a grand Republic.

And yet the follow-up to come may be assuring, the growth snipped, no need for alarm, no fear of Apocalypse, stay on the path, stick to the prescribed plan, be sure to do your part, and you'll see mountain laurel like never before. Eyes alert to the blossom and the branch, you'll take a hike in the light of an orange sun. These lessons your old friend offers and these you have learned. When a gathering takes place along a ridgeline, you'll say remember and he'll say predict. Okay, you'll agree, if we start from here, we will go forward. The only direction the knees bend, he'll joke but then you'll add, that's an old story. Let's see how this new one progresses. We can walk. We'll get there and when we reach that fence, we can climb over or we can find a gate, open it, and then pass through it to the next mown field.

In the Public Garden

It is our oasis in this suburb, shrine to a thought provided shape. It whispers to us, something about mutability in an age of steel. Some might sit for a moment and trace letters or retreat behind a parapet so that signification offers an answer to desire unfilled. Some might miss the point, wonder what necessitates such a reason for being and frustrated shun its light.

II

I could stay out here forever, he thought.

He could see that Alice had fallen asleep. With her sun bonnet pulled low over her eyes, her arms crossed on her chest and feet propped upon the seat of an empty chair, he could see her breathing deeply, calm and asleep.

Her sunglasses hid her eyes, but his eyes took in the cathedral, the old town hall, and the many cafes that lined the central square.

He looked at the people: those who sat sipping a beverage and those who moved quickly on their way to an appointment at the physician's perhaps or to a meeting with an estate agent.

It did seem to be a lovely place to live. They had been here for a week and he at least felt reluctant to be leaving the next day.

It had been a lovely holiday. They had reserved this day for relaxation – some shopping perhaps and short walks about the historic center.

Alice stretched and then asked her husband the time.

"Two o'clock," he replied.

"Good God," she said. "We've been here all this time. Nearly two hours."

"I don't mind," he said reaching across the small café table to hold her hand.

"You may not mind. But they may," she said pointing toward the wait-staff with her free hand. "Two hours and all we've had is a coffee and a tea."

"I don't think they mind. No one has rushed us along. No one, in fact, has bothered us at all."

She shook her head in disbelief.

"I can leave a big tip," he said, adding, "We'll be leaving tomorrow."

And Alice said, "Perhaps we should leave now."

He seemed taken aback, but Alice reassuringly said, "I mean for the hotel."

And so, they got up. He did leave a generous tip. Arm-in-arm they slowly strolled in the direction of their hotel.

Along the river bank other visitors bent over to feed the ducks waddling there on the gravel paths between river and street. A glass covered tour boat slid by as a tape ran in several languages, none quite discernible at the place they stood still locked arm-in-arm.

At the hotel a doorman tapped his hat in greeting. The thick carpet inside felt so different from the gravel of the path and the concrete of the sidewalk.

When they reached their room Alice could not open the door. She waved the card key one way and another and every way she could think of and yet nothing happened; the red light in the lock would not turn green.

Sam grabbed the card and said with authority, "Here, let me try."

The results were no different. Flip the card-key as he did, the red light did not turn green.

"That's odd," he said. "Wait here. I'll go back down to the front desk."

"I'm going with you," Alice said.

In the elevator they were quiet. When the door opened, they walked briskly to reception, but then slowed as they neared the long mahogany counter. They both saw their luggage. The red and silver ribbons indicated the three cases to be theirs, but why had hotel staff apparently packed and moved their belongings?

Sam became a bit agitated and Alice stroked his arm with a calming gesture as if to say now easy dear, keep calm.

Before he could speak the attendant dutifully smiled and said, "Ah, Mr. and Mrs. Appledorn. You forgot to check out."

Neither the smile nor the words worked to restore Sam's equilibrium.

Now he had moved from agitation to anger. Alice squeezed his arm.

"What do you mean we forgot to check out?" he asked.

"Well, it is far beyond the noon hour," the attendant replied and then added, "Don't worry, we were most respectful and neat with all of your things, but the other guests did want their room – the room that had been yours, you see."

"I don't understand."

"The new guests arrived. Our staff needed to clean."

"But we don't leave until tomorrow."

"Hold on a second, please. Let me double check," and he diligently typed on a keyboard and then stared at a screen.

"No. No," he said. "There it is: Appledorn, seven nights."

"Seven nights. I reserved our room for eight nights. I kept singing, 'Eight Days a Week' before we left. Isn't that right, Alice?"

"Why, yes. You did. Over and over again."

"But please, Mr. Appledorn – look here." And he swung the screen around so Sam could read it. "See," he added.

And Sam said, "Yes, I see it but that doesn't mean a thing. We leave tomorrow."

"That may be, Mr. Appledorn. But you can't stay here tonight."

"And why not?"

"Because all the rooms are booked. All the rooms are full. It's the start of Fashion Week. I doubt you'll find an empty room anywhere in the city, certainly not in the center."

"But we have a room. We have a room here."

"Had a room."

The manager came out of a small office set off to the side behind the reception desk. He wore glasses but seemed to glance over the lenses rather than through them.

He said nothing and just stood there waiting for someone else to initiate the next round.

Abruptly, Sam grabbed Alice's hand and said, "Let's go."

"Where?" she asked.

"I don't know. Back to the café," he instructed.

"What about our luggage?" she asked.

"We'll get it later," he said.

They left and as they did so the manager stood still with arms crossed on his chest and shook his head in disbelief.

The streets were now impossible. The roadways had turned into parking lots and the sidewalks over-flowed with extraordinarily tall and thin women.

Alice grabbed Sam's arm and yanked him back. "We better get our bags, I think."

"I suppose you're right," he agreed.

They retreated and reentered the hotel lobby. They pulled the telescopic handles of their luggage out to the extended position and proceeded to wheel their belongings toward the door.

"You forgot the night of your flight," the manager called out.

"What do you mean?" Sam asked across the space between them.

"You flew at night. When you landed here, we were well into a new day. Add your seven nights here and that's eight nights. Check your dates. See? Your mistake. Not ours."

Sam paused a moment. He considered what the manager had said. Then he reached for Alice's elbow and said, "Come on." He then edged her along toward the exit.

On the crowded walk he pulled a large suitcase and a small one. Alice had a large pocketbook and mid-size suitcase. The silver and red ribbons blew in the slight breeze, festive.

"Don't stare," Alice said as a group of models parted for the frustrated couple dragging their luggage.

"But they're so ... tall," Sam replied in a sort of plaintive whine as they kept their pace going they knew not where.

A man rounded the corner, also tall, also thin, but not attractive. He seemed damp, unwashed and at the same time eager to please.

He stood directly in front of Sam and Alice. He had stopped their retreat – or was it now an advance?

The man raised his hand, more in greeting than command, and introduced himself.

"I am Tsimpouki," he announced. "I will be your guide."

"We don't need a guide," Sam said. "We need a place for the night. We return home tomorrow."

"That will be difficult," Tsimpouki noted.

"What? Return home?" Alice prompted.

"No. That I cannot foretell. But you will not find a room for the night. It is Fashion Week. Did you not plan for this? Did you not know this?"

"I suppose not," Sam grumbled.

"Well, then you do need a guide – to find your way through this night of frivolity to the bright morning of sobriety."

They looked at one another. Then turned left toward the square with its cafes and tourist sites.

Tsimpouki cried out, "I offered."

They reached the square, near-empty on their first visit; crowded on this their likely final visit.

There was nowhere to sit, no empty seats and so they sat on their luggage. Nonetheless, a waiter promptly appeared and they ordered.

"Could you still stay here forever?" Alice asked. Yes, she could read her husband's mind.

And then the waiter arrived with their Café Americano and then the lights went off. The square plunged into darkness. Startled voices rose in surprise and in all the languages of the Babel tower or the glass covered tour boat.

Suddenly, bright electric colors in rainbow hues washed across the square. Music started and the first of the Fashion Shows commenced.

But poor Alice and poor Sam had no patience for pomp. They suffered fatigue and sought some safe and soft place to rest their weary heads before boarding their plane and returning to their home the next day.

Tsimpouki popped up again. "Feeling sleepy?" he asked. And then he reprimanded the couple. "I told you." He said and then disappeared.

The fireworks began. They had finished their coffees, but had nowhere to go.

Sam had an idea. "Let's go to the garden by the university. We'll wait there."

"Why can't we look for a room?" Alice wondered.

"Because it's so crowded. You heard. It's Fashion Week. I should have guessed. I should have known."

"You should have counted correctly," Alice had become both annoyed and uncomfortable. It is true, luggage does not make the most comfortable seating.

"Let's go," Sam said.

"Why not?" Alice replied.

The crowd parted to let them go on their way. But wherever they went more crowds, more lights, more fireworks and fashion models met them.

They were tired despite the strong coffee. Luckily, they found an empty bench in the botanical garden. They dosed off for some few moments until the rhythms of a hundred tambourines awoke them. They found themselves guests in the midst of a counter-event. Hundreds pounded their tambourines but not one of them had a stitch of clothing.

The sprinklers came on, soaking the couple. One of the revelers offered them a tambourine, an invitation to join them while their clothes dried.

"Let's get a cab to the airport and wait there," Alice suggested.

"But where will we find a cab?"

Tsimpouki appeared just then. "Allow me," he said.

He appeared to whistle, but they heard nothing.

A cab appeared and they got into it.

"To the airport," Sam commanded. And off they went.

But it was slow going: the lights, the music, the models and their frequent changes. The city aglow in fireworks and smoke, their driver had to swing left then right. A direct route had been rendered impossible because impassable.

And when they reached the airport, they found it transformed into a colossal casino. The roulette wheel spun round and round. Delayed passengers bet on planes.

We met at the entrance. I had been so busy looking for a woman waving a blue scarf or looking in the distance at Cesar Pelli's tower that I almost missed spotting Marianne in the crowd that had gathered there for the eleven o'clock tour. And it had been so many years since we had last seen one another that it may have been a miracle that we did recognize one another.

I saw the guide with the agreed upon blue scarf and hesitantly called out "Sara" and at just that moment another woman my age also called "Sara" and then we turned to look at one another. We were still for some moments of silence and thought, but after a beat we knew and then we hugged though a bit tentatively at first. Marianne's eyes moved in the direction of that distant tower.

We behaved well enough on the tour and agreed to meet the next day. I had wanted to buy a book at the museum shop but stopped in the bathroom and when I rejoined our group our guide, Sara, moved us along. I told Marianne that our leader had too much northern punctuality about her. I could not even look around at some elegant scarves in the shop. Marianne laughed at me, and I knew we were still friends.

She had come for a conference on current European architecture and its impulse toward uniformity. Something, she later told me, she thought untrue. And I had come to this city to deliver a lecture at the Università Cattolica del Sacro Cuore for the inauguration of their Women's Studies program – only the third such program in Italy. Talk about architecture! My lecture had been scheduled for a hall in the old monastery Sant' Ambrogio. Bramante updated the structure in 1497 and planes bombed it in 1943. Now we live in a period of cooperation; shared purpose more than co-existence and my lecture had a co-sponsor, the University of Milan, College of Veterinary Studies, founded in 1791.

There is rhyme and reason to this resume of facts. Italy may not have many Women's Studies programs, but it produces the highest number of veterinarians per capita of any country in Europe. It also has the highest per capita car ownership of any country in the world. Perhaps there is a connection.

I am not a Women's Studies scholar, but I am a feminist. I am, you see, the first to hold the Jeanette Donker-Voet Chair in Veterinarian Science at Utrecht University in the Netherlands. Donker-Voet was the first woman to graduate as a veterinarian from Utrecht, my country's only program. In her day she broke barriers, yes, but hit insurmountable walls, too. She could only find work in a small pet clinic; the fellows would not permit her to see to ailing livestock such as cows, horses, and pigs. But years later the fellows did name a small building after her and some years after that they did create the endowed chair that I occupy. When I first came to Utrecht as a student more than a decade after Donker-Voet's death, Marianne and I shared a flat, but I do not necessarily digress, I just place one fact out of its proper position. At Utrecht, I determined to work with large farm animals – and so I did. After graduating from our only program in the country, I went to Wouw and then to Terschelling. I do not practice so much anymore even though in Utrecht we have the largest veterinary hospital in Europe. Most of my time I teach, lecture, and do some research. I would like to do more of the latter but my role in some ways feels predetermined as if I am one of Theo Jansen's Strandbeest, a kinetic sculpture blown across Scheveningen beach. Words are like stones anyway. I will walk and talk some more – here, there, and anywhere asked. In this wander the right one, the precise one may yet be found.

That next morning as I waited for Marianne in the small garden at the rear of the hotel I thought of Amsterdam. I thought of home and growing up there. Our garden behind the Keizersgracht house had been so lush even though a small square of city quilt that one felt each May and June transported to Indonesia. My parents were proficient, expert in all that they performed: surgery to sailing. Oh, that lush greenery and here as I sat my revelry became spoiled by a cigarette smoker. No matter, moments later Marianne arrived and my mood lifted though definitely not like the rings puffed from that obnoxious fellow oblivious to anyone's discomfort or disapproval.

Marianne told me about an Italian television show of a decade ago, *Veterinario nella città*. She insisted that I must know all about it before

I prepare my lecture. I told her I had already done so and she said nonsense and spoke about a homeless man in Rome and an affluent woman in a grand palazzo and I found it all very confusing, irrelevant, and trite, and I wondered why she chatted so about a defunct RAI production and I wondered how she knew of it and I wondered why she told me nothing of her life.

We were walking together on the Via Alessandro Manzoni past expensive shops and fashionable hotels when we noticed a view of the Westerkerk tower with its crown at top in the window of a tourist agency and Marianne paused, looked at me, took my hand amidst the crowd of walkers in the city and asked:

"Do you miss Amsterdam?"

"Yes," I said. "Terribly."

"I do and I do not," she said. "You see, after Utrecht going home to Abcoude had been impossible."

"Of course," I said. "Who goes home after university?"

"Well, I did think about it. It is a lovely town and commutable."

"On the slow train."

"Yes, Jacqueline. You are correct: on the slow train."

"Utrecht is not Amsterdam as Hartford is not New York. Nor Lelystad, Leiden. But I am happy."

"And Milan is not Paris."

"But here we are."

"Yes, here we are."

And we continued with our walk. We went in the direction of the Duomo with no intention of touring it or shopping at La Rinascente or anywhere or anything else. We walked and talked, but eventually stopped at one café with street-side seating. I had a most delicious iced-coffee, quite extraordinary and memorable and sweet and that is why I mention it here or is it because of what Marianne said to me then and the tone in which she said it?

Fifty years of age differs mightily from twenty. We had recalled how pretty we were in those Utrecht years. How we drove boys crazy one night at a party. How we flirted and laughed, but such a strange laugh. *How pretty we were* -- we strove, I think, to reassure one another how striking we remained. Perhaps. Who among us believes her own words? And Marianne told me of her work and a little bit about her children too. She regretted that her major work would be the renovation of the Cafe Cromhuis at the Bijbels Museum in Amsterdam. With interiors by Jacob de Wit, she felt overwhelmed and also less than challenged since she had just the Café to renovate. And then there had been the restriction placed on her to incorporate and preserve the mural by Charles Aussems, an artist (Austrian no less) that no one in the Netherlands seems to know anything about. The café has not been updated since the museum moved to its spacious Herengracht location in the mid-1970s. I told Marianne we were children then. And she said that how she wanted to open the museum café somehow to the wonderful garden, Aussems's mural be damned.

Marianne knew not how she could fulfill her vision for this space and I knew not what I would say in my lecture. Women's Studies be damned. The program would open, yes, and the men and women who took the courses would learn to re-engineer their lives and yet Europe seemed to say Arabs must remain in their place and women must return to their place. Scullery-maids all.

In the Giardini Pubblici, my favorite place in Milan, I had seen a turtle. It moved slowly across a wide broken tree branch in one of the ponds. It moved as turtles tend to move and I told myself then and I told myself there, go slow, be as the turtle sure and cautious and remember that in some cultures it is not an Atlas as at the Dam Palace that holds up the earth, but a turtle – strong, certain, and, okay, maybe a little slow. But dependable. Yes, I know so. *Lo so*, as they would say here. Only at the end of the journey we might imagine the possible. Something more than a walk together to Coin for new leather wallets at fifty percent off.

I asked Marianne if she could remember how pretty we were that night in Utrecht when we went to the party in the Wilhelmina Park and how we had teased some of the boys there. Marianne asked if I remembered the tall medical student with red hair, hair that fell into his eyes and that he knocked again and again with an orchestra's director's gesture out of his eyes and I said indeed I do. His gesture had been so strange that all these years later I can still recall it, yes, and

Marianne said he is my husband. And I said, good for you, Marianne. Good for you.

And I wondered what I would say to the young women at my lecture, young women and a few boyfriends, I imagined. What point should I make? What should I say? Should I stick to historical facts, offer encouragement, or utter a stern warning?

I have to say something, offer some point of orientation – say it, speak it: but words are stone. They form no cairns.

"Tell them of your struggles," Marianne had said. "And of your success."

"Success?" I echoed.

What must I say? Tell the anti-Europeans that through the European Credit Transfer and Accumulation System they could come to Utrecht for a semester and our students could study here and all of this can be done with ease. Nothing to worry about, smooth transitions all around. I had spent a year arranging all the agreements and corresponding documents that our veterinary students needed. I spent that year, too, dreaming of cows on Terschelling and horses at the Hollandse Manege in Amsterdam. No man walking beside me. No man of red hair or athletic build. Just study and work and again Marianne, my friend.

She recalled flirtations. I remembered our bucket brigade the night of the storm that soaked our floors and walls, but by bailing water out as fast as it leaked through, we managed to protect our priceless graduate school possessions. All those notes for papers on topics no one else, so we thought then, had ever considered before. Papers we would write and the world would read! So, we thought then.

"Marianne, I must tell you how thankful I was to land at Linate. The flight, yes, it is brief, but the man next to me drank cranberry juice and vodka the whole way, one after the other, and he pushed his tray up and then pulled it down and he coughed again and again, a hacking cough. When we landed, he pulled from his carry-on a sun-visor and placed it on his bulbous head. Marianne, I must tell you how I so disliked this man and had been glad to be rid of him. But then the next day, who did I see during my walk in the Giardini Pubblici but this man. I nodded politely. He said hello."

"Jacqueline, you must come and visit. You must meet Matthijs."

"And the children."

"Yes, of course. And the children. And I will show you the Bijbels Museum."

"But I thought you were an atheist?" I joked.

"And we will dine in the Café Cromhuis."

"And we will walk in the garden."

"And we will come inside and rearrange all the buildings, the tiny buildings in the model of old Jerusalem."

"Yes, together we will update entire cities as you will update the Cafe; not as Presidents and Prime Ministers, but as artists and scientists."

There is no map of the ancient or future city. Let each find her own path.

Marianne said that I suffer from the great fear, that silence was no solution. I must have something to say, to offer.

I returned to my hotel room that night, emptied four bags of the purchases I had made and filled each one with all the love that beat in my wounded heart. In the near-darkness of the city at night I went into the Giardini Pubblici, strapped a bag onto the muzzle of each of the four horses of the apocalypse sculpture, left the horses there to munch away to their hearts' content, and I turned back toward my third-floor, courtside room to write the inspiring speech I soon must deliver.

Gianni walked down the street to see if his car had been sold. To his chagrin, there it sat, apparently unmoved as well as unsold, the large banner price still affixed to the front windshield. He had tried to convince the owner of the lot to affix not a price but a name – his – Gianni – in the belief that association with the realm of stardom would assure a quick sale. But the salesman recognized neither the name nor its namesake's face. He told Gianni he would have a large sum for him if he waited until he sold it, otherwise he would have to settle for a sum remarkably lower than its worth if he opted for immediate cash.

He walked up the street, packed his bags, and left for the airport. He observed that several long gray hairs curled out of the opening in his V-neck sweater. He would have to pull them before boarding the plane. In New York he'd want to look nineteen again.

On the plane the man next to him listened to a familiar song. Gianni could make out the melody when his neighbor took a plug from an ear to request some water as a flight attendant passed. Gianni recognized it so quickly for it was one of his, one he had recorded – was it that long ago?

He turned to his neighbor, smiled, and said, "Good song."

And his neighbor for the coast-to-coast flight said, "I've heard better ones."

"Well," Gianni started to reply but the other fellow inserted the earpiece, turned toward the window, and closed his eyes.

In New York he went through security and no eye brow raised either thinking Gianni a threat to national security or recalling those songs of yesteryear.

When he stepped outside Fred and Alice were there to greet him. They wore shoulder pads and football helmets and held high a large sign that said GO Gianni GO.

"Oh, Gianni," Fred said, "we're so glad to see you."

"What's with the sporting attire?" He asked.

"Oh, Gianni," Alice said. "We wanted to be sure you recognized us. It's been so long."

"Good thing you left your chin strap unbuttoned. Otherwise, I may not have recognized your distinguished chin," Gianni joked.

And Fred and Alice both exclaimed, "Oh, Gianni."

"Hey, how do you get a cab around here?" He asked.

"We have an Uber waiting for us over there," and Fred pointed across the access road to a red Buick Enclave.

Once seated in their ride Alice asked Gianni what he would like to do first and rattled off a rapid-fire list of possibilities.

Gianni said, "Gee, guys. I think I'd like to check in and then go for a walk by myself to get acclimated, to get readjusted. It's been so long."

On his walk he saw the Brill Building where so many years before he had watched several rough-cut screenings of his films. In those days he kept his home close to his origins and had not made the move west, had not made that near permanent move.

He had returned to New York to perform in a non-musical production of *Turandot*. This drama would feature a new ending something neither Puccini, Alfano, nor Berio had ever imagined, something new and different and startling from the mind of Broadway's newest genius: Max Stern. No "Nessun Dorma" in this version, no soccer match music for Max. No music.

The lights faded. A moment later the title receded from the screen, he saw his name spread across it: Gianni Onderdonck, even before the director's.

He saw the young Swanson couple board the bus. He knew that he would be found seated by the aisle near the front when they entered. Gianni did not care for the Mrs. Swanson as a person though as a character the script-writers did intend for some attraction between them. As a person he recalled that he found the husband much more interesting though as a character he had been constructed very much as a dunce and a minor character though one with a college letterman's appeal.

He saw that the bride made eye contact as she walked past. An exterior showed the bus climbing a hill on a winding road and then descending. The weather had turned frightful. Off to the side some rocks broke free and tumbled down. The bus driver slammed the brakes, but it was no good. The bus rolled once and then again. It stopped as steam rose from it. The driver's wide-eyes indicated death. But the Swansons and their companion stranger miraculously survived. They crawled out of the bus. They stood and wiped themselves free of debris.

Gianni heard himself say (as he knew he would), "Come. I know somewhere nearby. We may rest there. Come. I know."

The Swansons exchanged doubtful glances, but what alternatives did the newlyweds have on that wretched night of cold mist and fog?

"Well, alright," the young husband replied. "I suppose it's a plan at any rate. Best to keep moving," he said.

The Mrs. shook once and then twice and turned from one man to the other.

They started to walk. Then Gianni saw them walking away. Then he saw a large house, a dark house. Then they walked. Then they had arrived at the door.

Gianni heard the chimes. After a pause that allowed the three to offer their skill at quizzical expression, the latches came undone and the door opened. There, stood Gianni's co-star.

The sallow faced man offered his greetings and apologized. He noted that his servant had the evening off. When he ushered the three impromptu guests into his house he looked deeply into Gianni's eyes and nodded at him and Gianni returned the gesture, but added the words, "And so I have returned my dear Elgar."

At this point the music became more pronounced. It carried a certain familiarity but also a sentimentality that for fans of the two – and yes, they were legion -- would bring on tears and an accelerated heartbeat.

Elgar said in a pronounced slow monotone, "Please, enter. I will show you to your rooms. This is a horrid night. One of misfortune, I presume?"

At the word "horrid" the camera caught Gianni in a distressed expression, exaggerated for an extra beat to be sure the expression and all it expressed could not be missed.

Ken found the box in the back of the old Gloria Hill Studio. Clean out day, he supposed, and he made out like gold.

He took it home and there ran a few of the reels through an old movie-o-la. He recognized the performer: a young Gianni Onderdonck wearing a kilt and a t-shirt with a palm tree on it and hamming-up for the camera. Ken knew right away what he would do. He would edit this material in ways that might surprise Sergei Eisenstein. He would add a contemporary heavy metal soundtrack and Gianni himself would record a voice-over narration.

Crane shots and crane shots of crane shots. Tracking shots and tracking shots of tracking shots. Gianni yells something and then the man exits the subway again. The other man crosses the street. We see the gun. Then one man falls while the other drops the gun and keeps walking. Gianni says, "Okay. That's better."

He sleeps and dreams and there on the screen are the images he dreams. There is a warehouse full of a life's possessions. There is a curl of smoke stretching skyward. He wakes and dresses for his meeting with the insurance representative.

We see Gianni curled tight into a ball as Max Stern describes the project. Fred and Alice get more and more excited. Fred begins to jump up and down in joy. Gianni winds himself into a tighter ball. Fred stumbles, grabs his ankle, sits down, and moans.

Max senses Gianni's doubt. He comes over to Gianni and pulls him from the sofa.

"Look, Gianni," he says. "This is now and no longer then. This is the bell that will ring and the light that will shine and your hand will be the hand to flip the switch into the on position. The on position, Gianni. Now, now let us begin!"

Alice came over to where they stood. She looked at Gianni and said, "Oh, isn't he wonderful" and then she turned to Max and repeated, "Isn't he wonderful?" She embraced them and then Fred cried out, "Now come on you guys. That's my wife!"

The Swanson girl looked frightened when she caught Elgar staring at her.

Elgar turned toward Gianni. Then the Swanson girl shivered as if she had seen a ghost.

Elgar reminded his guests to make themselves at home. He reached for Gianni's elbow and gently led him to the side of the room, far from its fire and deep in the shadows where they could not be overheard.

"So, Olaf. We meet again," Elgar said.

Gianni glanced toward the Swansons. They looked into each other's eyes, held hands, and seemed oblivious to their host and their fellow guest.

Gianni turned back to Elgar as he spoke again. He had become noticeably agitated, anxious.

"I see you are interested in the girl," Elgar said.

"Not in that way," Gianni replied.

The music had started again as Elgar shook his head.

"Oh, Olaf. There can be no escape. We will always have Tisbury."

"No, no," Gianni replied, uncertain.

"Always, yes," Elgar continued. "Not only the living, but also the dead."

Lightning struck outside the windows. It was not distant. The music became more pronounced. A shadow figure could be seen in the hall.

Ken found out how to contact Gianni. By luck, they connected on the first try.

"Hello. Gianni Onderdonck?"

"Yes."

"This is Ken Matthews."

"Yes."

"Is this a good time?"

"Well, I honestly don't know. Is it? You tell me."

"Can we talk for a few minutes?"

"It seems we are talking. Aren't we?"

"Look, Gianni. I appreciate this. I appreciate you taking the time out of your day..."

"Take it. Please, take it. Save me from Max Stern. Save me from the New York stage."

"Well, I just might be able to help. I am a filmmaker."

"I haven't worked in years."

"I know. I mean that's a shame, an injustice, our loss."

"Perhaps."

"Look, I got this footage of you."

"So."

"I found it at the dump. I went to drop off old stereo equipment and out of a box I could see some strands. I bent down and pulled and there were a couple of reels. Are you still there?"

"I'm listening."

"I took it home. Looked at it. It's you, all of you – hamming it up."

"Ah, the Follies."

"What's that?"

"The Follies. Something we did for fun back then. Something to loosen up before the serious work that'd follow."

"Can I use it?"

"Be my guest."

"What I want to do is to record you, a voice-over. To begin it as an interview. Then let the questions fade out as you start to sing."

Fred and Alice as Ping and Pong. The ever so wonderful, so versatile Fred and Alice. Imagine!

Exactly, Gianni worried.

"But ..." he began.

Max would have none of it and waved-off Gianni's concern with an extended hand and the rapid counter fire of "Tut. Tut. Tut."

"Tut. Tut. Tut."

Max took a lamp and held it under his chin and growled, "Vincerò!"

"A voice-over."

"No script?"

"No script. You ad-lib."

"Mama mia! What are you, nuts?"

As per November 1, 1939 addendum:

No approval shall be given to the use of words and phrases in motion pictures including but not limited to, the following:

Hand over hand. And the legs push up forcing each vertical step against the tall stone ledge. Easier it would have been by far to take the winding, haphazardly paved road. But what then is the point? And that way the hands and legs may be saved but the view is impaired. Of course, coming this way one must first walk through the field of bison – and pray – before commencing the assent – and, indeed, during the climb as well. But none have ever been gored and none have fallen. There's always a first time one might think: more likely think than say for who wants to be seen as weak?

And the road misses the summit, the clear rock of it from which the towers of a distant metropolis can be seen. Below the bison look like game pieces moping about a game-board; that is, enclosed and kept. Their owner's house, so large at the swoop end of its drive, seems dollhouse size. No one worries about trespassers, no one appears to be at home. Behind the house a small gap in the growth opens to the narrow trail that soon arrow-like shoots up. Nothing can be more enjoyable than the upward climb – pull-up followed by deep-knee bend. No stop until the top. No Pop-Tart nor Tang until the top.

Then look around: the fields, the forests, the lakes, and the towers of a distant city. Granite beneath one's feet. Rest a moment. None are ready to go just yet. To go, perhaps, to the camp and in the long-house claim a headdress, carry it out, and back to town to be stored in a basement. Then to go to a cabin back downhill, open an unlocked window, climb (this time) inside to rooms of furs and Rosicrucian pamphlets. Who are they? What do they believe? Not to be asked or answered – what had happened here? Not to be guessed.

At the pool of stone on the way back, the long way, half a group cools off without clothes and looking up through the trees toward the light. Others keep the headdress, furs, and pamphlets off the ground, away from the water, too. They are impatient and wonder about contacting the police but know that to do so would be seen as weak.

Will not suggest it. Everyone wonders, who were those people; what is a Rosicrucian? And one says, the headdress offends him and that explains his liberating it for his people. Campers, he says. What of my people? He adds.

The front section of the paper has more in it than the others and yet nothing about the cabin, the furs, or the Rosicrucian. Was there some blood along the edges? If the headdress was a lark, what then the cabin? Sure, they could go hand over hand up the cliff-side after daring those cross-eyed bison, but none of them had counted on an unlocked window and what they found inside.

One watched outside his window how branches and their leaves blew side to side. Was it violent? But then again, he could see the purple flowers, unless he slept and so many furs wrapped him, smothered him. The cabin had been sealed up too long, he reasoned, and that accounted for the smell. And his mom, a grammar school teacher in town. What to do? He worried about right and wrong; strength and weakness, too.

So, he tried to think only of the climb; not the bison nor the view; not the snacks nor the headdress; not the pool of stone nor the unclothed swimmers. Hand over hand and push up with the full force of one's legs. Those furs, those pamphlets and these questions – so many of them – regarding belief, but also practice. He wondered: did they sing?

They rode six miles out from town. They locked their bikes by the fence and had no choice but to return for them. Maybe next year a car, or surely the next. They dropped the furs and pamphlets, but carried the headdress, and as they pedaled, all feathers blew back toward a place they had so abruptly left and did not know.

Had they seen some spirit – a woman of the wilderness, a harbinger of something prophetic or uncertain? A devil perhaps and who would be so weak as to squirm?

The newspaper recorded nothing. It let nothing be known. One day went by and a second one. They began to feel less stressed, stronger too. And resumed with confidence their practice. Yet they wondered what secret knowledge had become theirs, theirs only? Locked now into a fraternity, a brotherhood of happenstance they would have to keep its secrets and abide by its rituals and rules. Inarticulate; unacknowledged, even so.

There would be three-hundred and seventy-five in the graduating class but less than a quarter of that number would attend a reunion one-half century later. The lights would be dim; the music intrusive, nostalgic; decades old. Red and green colors would swirl as if a holiday display. And on to this stage, he'd enter.

He spoke to one standing there, familiar yet obviously older though still recognizable, too. He said, "… and through the field that day, past the bison …"

"No," the other said, "not quickly past the bulls but slowly near the Guernsey cows."

He said, "And all that way with the headdress in our hands …"

And again that no. "No," the other said. "We took it down from off its hook on the wall by the fire pit. Put it on. Snapped a photo and returned it to the place where we had found it."

"But what of the furs and the Rosicrucian pamphlets?"

"We unlocked our bikes from the rail of the bridge and pedaled home."

"What of the blood?"

"Yes, we remain blood brothers. Don't be so weak. Say nothing. Actions can be louder than words."

They shook hands, one hand over the other hand.

While he was there, he danced the Mashed Potato and he danced the Twist. He even twice danced the Freddy. He knew most of his partners and they knew him. Everyone got tired, some left. The night unwound. The light had been so slow to arrive.

Eddie and Lucinda

"Death intervenes to simplify everything. Every doubt, every misgiving, every uncertainty is swept aside by the greatest belittler of them all, which is death." Philip Roth, *The Human Stain*

Eddie opens the driver's side door of a green car with light tan leather seats. He wears polished loafers, pressed khaki pants, and a neatly ironed cotton shirt. His hair is combed; his beard, trimmed. He sits in the driver's seat, Lucinda beside him. He puts the key in the ignition, adjusts the volume on the radio, and drives off.

"All I'm saying is," Eddie began.

"Yes," Lucinda interrupted.

"We can't move to California."

"Why not," she asked.

"We've already made our purchase."

"I told you we shouldn't," she said. "I told you we should wait."

"Well, I thought we should buy – no time like the present."

Of course, some people don't like to drive a car or to make the big decisions about where they are going. Eddie and Lucinda would have none of it. They believed that they accurately saw the situation, opportunity, and potential, although occasionally they might disagree about that vision. One might, indeed, render the other hesitant, unsettled. Yet, they surmised such difficulties would make them stronger and better. After such debate they might conclude that they would not succumb, they would not be absorbed by the center.

"We could move back later," she conjectured, somewhat hesitantly offered as if searching hard for compromise and reconciliation.

"I don't know," he said tentatively. "That would be disruptive, don't you think?" He paused, thought a moment, and added, "not so much for us, but for the others: those left behind."

"Would we, could we care at that point?" Lucinda looked out the car window into the distance, speculative.

"But we should care. Shouldn't we?" His two hands held the wheel loosely, almost boastful in gesture, the car long ago repaired and still running smooth.

"Don't worry so much about the future," she decided, "a future you can neither control nor influence."

"Ah, yes. But you were all for planning once we decided on the purchase. And that, at least, implies a belief in influence if not control."

An iron rain fell across the city, but did not touch the suburbs where it stayed clear and bright. Near an exit, some people could be seen floating in old tires and because the rain had so much iron in it, those people did not move. They appeared as if composed in a documentary photograph, a social issue.

Lucinda turned away from the scene outside and toward Eddie and continued: "But now I've seen California and my outlook has changed."

"We can make a purchase there, too -- if you like?" Eddie offered.

"But what would we do with what we bought here?"

"And it was so hard to get in…"

"The forms…"

"The waitlist…"

"The price… I don't know…" Lucinda hesitated.

Eddie's will would be steel. Sternly, he told her, "Now you're getting cold feet."

An association with the word *cold* led him to think of the swimming pool, how there used to be more shade but over the winter one grand old tree fell over during a storm. Spring came and a work crew removed the tree and repaired the pool. Summer arrived, and once again he sat by the pool. He wore a shirt this summer which he did not remove whereas the prior summer he wore no shirt and when not in the shade or in the pool, he basked in direct sun.

"I'm not sure what you mean," Lucinda's words brought Eddie back to the present, to driving the car and continuing the conversation.

"We can make arrangements," he said. "That's what people do. We could be shipped," he added, morbidly.

"Enough already," Lucinda laughed.

"They have refrigeration, you know," Eddie joked.

"What if we don't arrive at the same time?"

"You mean go."

"That's possible. And you don't like to travel."

"Why don't we sell here and buy there?" Eddie suggested, turning a bit more serious.

"But, Eddie," Lucinda countered, "you had your heart set on that hillside."

"They have bigger hills in California."

"But do they have history? Do they have community, Eddie, like we do?'

"At the moment," Eddie said and paused for a beat, "they have neither our money nor our flesh."

Lucinda kept the joke going, "And, I would add," she said, "not yet our bones."

"You always must get in the last word, mustn't you, Lucinda?"

"Yes," she replied.

And the car sped down the highway. It hummed. It ran exceptionally smooth. Eddie realized that someday the car too would be a wreck.

The Wind and the Rain

We left Madison Port moments after twelve noon. Not a cloud in the sky, and children galloped about the foredeck in front of their family's parked vehicle while out beyond Brighton Light fishermen fished for blue fish. Sitting there in the calm, enjoying the sun we thought little of home and less of work. It wouldn't be long before we reached the other shore, entered our vehicles, and drove off. For now, though, the salt-sea air seemed an elixir of sorts. At least for me the smooth motion and sweet smell offered relief from the hubbub of work-life. Until, that is, a slight sea-breeze blew diesel fumes back toward our section of the seating. As the vile odor receded, breeze became wind and all heck broke out as deckchairs slid to one side and children retreated to the arms of worried parents.

A darkening sky now hid the sun from view. Most passengers retreated to their trucks and cars. Our ship seemed to crackle and groan on the ever-enlarging waves. We were farther from the city, not closer now, and pushed, it seemed, eastward. True, we swirled as in a whirlpool. Back and forth for hours upon hours – so wild and fraught a night.

And when we woke the next morning, we found ourselves, some of us, washed ashore on some unrecognizable split of sand, still clinging to a barrel stave, chrome bumper, or picnic basket. We knew not what became of the rest of the crew and passengers, but here we were for the moment safe. There must have been a mere twenty of us on the beach whereas there may have been more than two-hundred on the boat.

It gladdened me to no end that my spouse had survived with me. We had little recall of the occurrence, but, apparently, we both had held tight to a leather football endorsed by one Gayle Sayers and this mere bobble-float proved sufficient to save our lives. Before the tossing and churning, Julie Ottani, a young physical therapist had introduced herself to us and, low and behold, she too had survived and washed ashore with us on this beach.

She turned to us and started to speak after first choking and coughing some sea-water.

"I know this place," she said.

"Where are we?" my wife asked.

"I am certain we are on Swanson's Island."

"How can you be sure," my wife – Alice – asked.

"Well, I'm not entirely sure." Sea air had erased the faces of several wooden buildings. "I came to this place, I think, on a trip during college."

"Like a frat party?" I queried.

"No, no," Julie said. "For class. Swanson's Island is – was – a government research facility. A lab: anthrax and that sort of thing. At least, that was our speculation. Me and the rest of the class."

"So where is everybody?" I asked.

Julie paused for a moment, looked around at the others rising from the sand like sunbaked lizards, and then said, "Oh, the government abandoned this place years ago."

I noticed a small spot of blood appear on her lower arm. From such a little gap in the skin, the bleeding seemed profuse.

"Your arm," I said.

"Yes," Julie added, an offer for me to continue after I had momentarily paused.

I took the opportunity. "It's bleeding," I said, pointing at the same time.

She looked at her arm. "Yes, it is, isn't it?" And then she looked at me. "So is yours."

Across the beach other survivors expressed surprise or shock. We all seemed to be bleeding from our forearms.

I reached out for Alice who had been so quiet all this time, but my arms did not reach her nor did hers reach me.

Julie's neck elongated as her arms became shorter. Everyone's head – mine included I supposed – shrank and became birdlike. And yet I felt no alarm. After the initial moments of blood dripping, we became calm, oddly acquiescent with what had occurred.

Our lower bodies remained as before, but above the navel we had become wild-turkeys and although speech as we had known it no longer could be produced, we, nonetheless, were able to communicate one with another.

The beach became a playground of sorts as some of us ran back and forth testing and perhaps even beginning to enjoy these new bodies of ours. Then it was discovered that we could fly. Yes, we could both run on the ground and fly in the air. What marvel of nature had happened here?

True, many of us moved awkwardly at first. The scene appeared a bit like carnival bumper cars. Luckily, no one got injured during this mayhem of adjustment. Indeed, laughter prevailed throughout the afternoon—though an unrecognizable sort of glee, something more guttural than expected or perhaps not so unexpected, to be honest.

Frolic concluded at nightfall as hunger arrived for each of us. One no longer felt like being silly at that point. Something somber had replace mirth. Now what? This split of sand offered not so much a seed or a snail upon it. The installation had long ago been abandoned, dismantled, and raked under the dunes.

Alice made a suggestion and all of us accepted the plan to fly west to more populated places. We must have looked like demented Valkyries as our group of about twenty jostled for balance in newborn and still awkward flight. What a view we enjoyed, especially as we approached the first of many bridges, their lights aglow and colorful. Favorable winds aided our limited skill and soon an outlying city came into view and then, then we saw the largest of the large – our beloved metropolis.

We tried to land as best we could but it was not easy so new were we to the idea of flight, we skidded and slid. And quite frankly those on the ground did not open their arms and offer food and drink. Perhaps donuts would have been hard to swallow and coffee not as sweet as sea-water. Instead, they ran from us and then, for the first time in this adventure of strange metamorphosis, we were afraid.

They returned armed with weapons and shouted at us, raised their fists at us. We grew hungry. Our journey here had been hard and we sought solace as well as nourishment. Our necks ached. It began to rain, a mere drizzle at first, and then a hard rain that hit everybody and everybody felt more than a little bit uncomfortable. All of us there together in that storm.

We dream at night of reverent words knowing the next day may sting us like a viper. We wake when hounded by an artillery barrage; cry to our parents to make the smoke lift and the morning lighter. There are places that must be ours, far from the vendor's salted cod; safe, quiet places of bucolic summer, beautiful rooms. Climb into memory even though all scaffolding is by its nature dangerous. Apply this general law to the particulars below. Who hears the tune? Who sees the swings?

*

"What time are Nick and Rosie due to arrive?" the man of the house inquired of his spouse.

"Her name is Rose," she said on the downbeat of a knife slicing through an onion.

"Yes, but a Rose...," he began in a sing-song voice.

"... by any other name is still a rose. Yes, I know," she finished for him and waved the knife in the air as she did so as if a conductor with a baton.

"Yes, but you don't know that from now on she shall be known as Rosalyn."

She ignored him for a moment and concentrated on that onion. Then she looked up and informed him: "You do have a grandson, you know."

"And his name?" he asked absentmindedly and adding, "I still don't know when to expect them, and I need to know so that I'll be ready for their arrival." He paused a moment. Regally he announced, "The trumpets then shall sound!"

"And his name is Matt."

"Whose name?"

"Your grandson's."

"Yes, of course," he said rather curt. "I knew that."

She glared at him -- the onion still not completely sliced.

He glared right back at her and said, "Why do you look at me like that. Matt, yes," he said. "Matt: short for Matthew, one would suppose."

She continued slicing onions, now having moved on to a second one. She began now to chop the slices, unsure if he was joking or teasing or something far worse.

"I still don't know when they are supposed to get here," he whined.

"About one o'clock," she said hoping to appease him for a few minutes while she finished the onions and started to tear-up.

He had always been the better cook, but now he arranged and re-arranged silverware and talked almost non-stop and had stopped so much as boiling water for tea.

"I see," he said to no one in particular. He glanced downward and added, "Why can't we sit on the floor?"

"What did you say?" she asked.

And he replied sternly, annoyed, "I said, 'I see'."

"Not 'we'll see'," she offered as if to lighten his mood.

"No, no. Not that." He remained somewhat grim. He looked directly at her and said, "Stop the cart."

"What's that?" she asked.

"If you stop the cart," he spoke slowly now, "I can easily climb down."

She stopped what she had been doing, her cooking or the prep work that precedes it, and asked, "Are you dreaming of the bison again?"

He looked out the large kitchen window that provided a view of their large backyard and replied, "No, not the bison; the coach and the team."

They could breathe easy now. There would be little talk of conspiracy in the days to follow and much more emphasis on cooperation and planning. It seemed as if a storm had been weathered and that after three days – or years – of darkness a bright sun had come out, had returned to foster growth and possibility, but the onions had started to stick in the pan and the phone rang and then it seemed someone had knocked at the front door.

She answered the phone; he, the door as is their practice, their division of labor even now. He brought the delivery into the kitchen.

"Now we have a centerpiece, flowers for the table," he said.

And she said, "Aren't they lovely," and then asked, "Who are they from?" The phone call apparently had been either a very brief one or a wrong number.

"It doesn't say anything. There doesn't seem to be a card or a receipt." He inspected the bouquet closely, walked around it to take in all facts to be so gathered.

She seemed to reach for the missing note, to grab it out of thin air, to force it to appear and as she did so she remarked, "Why would we get a receipt? The sender gets the receipt. We get the greeting."

"Found it," he called out enthusiastically, happy to have beaten her to the reward. "It says: 'Whatever is beautiful, whatever is meaningful, whatever brings health and happiness, may it be yours'."

The words had stirred her. "Why, that's lovely," she said and then asked, "Who are they from?"

He turned the card over in his hand and turned it again. He looked up and said, mystified, "It doesn't say."

Impatient and perhaps exasperated she told him, "What do you mean: 'it doesn't say'? It must say who sent them."

He felt victorious when he conjectured, "What difference does it make. It's nice. Now we have a centerpiece for the table."

She paused and seemed to search for a new tact to take. After a moment she had it: "Did you give the delivery man a tip?"

"It could have been a woman," he countered.

"Delivery person then," she replied and returned to her unanswered question: "Did you?"

"No," he confessed. "I know how much they charge for flowers. That's expense enough." He lifted his hands up toward his face as if reciting a benediction. "Believe me, a tip gets worked in to the price."

"Honestly," she had become flustered. She walked to the dining room to see where he had placed the arrangement. Satisfied, she returned to the kitchen.

"What time do they get here?" he asked.

*

"Did the stain come out?" she asked.

"I don't know," he said, paused a moment and then added, "I don't know why we hang wash outside this time of year."

"It's good for the environment."

"But it doesn't dry."

"It saves electricity."

"It freezes."

He had dreamed of the giant again, the muscleman turned toward his city of towers and steeples as if to say "this is mine." He had dreamed that the giant lost his skin and tuned his palms in supplication or prayer. A row of trees along the distant road swayed in the wind, but the giant would not be moved no matter how pierced with pain.

He returned to the present, examined the cloth, and proclaimed: "It is gone now, clear and clean and icy too."

"Children can be so messy."

"And so too their parents."

"They also are gone now."

"And we can return to quiet."

"And cleanliness too."

"Ah, yes. Right next to godliness."

They stood together in their large back yard, unpinning laundry, folding it, and placing it in a plastic blue basket to bring it inside.

A piano sonata played on the kitchen radio. They both knew it to be one of Beethoven's but for the life of them they could not remember the total number he had written.

Our reputation had deteriorated. Fifty years ago, the advertisements cried out that after you've seen this place "nothing else will compare. Nothing Else!" and "There's nothing like it this side of Park Avenue" – some very confusing geography. But it is true, no sooner were these three buildings with a pool and shared courtyard opened and occupied, then there were problems with trash collection and leaky roofs. The developer had also built the arena at the state university and that roof did not leak. Still the complex for years to most neighbors seemed a well-established choice for those who had either saved or invested well and sold their sprawling ranches or Queen Anne manors for the elegance and graciousness of refined condominium living on the city's western edge.

Lately though some of the townspeople who reside in single family homes had begun to grow weary of their more densely housed yet equally affluent neighbors. They grew despondent at the increase in bright lights and sirens in the early morning hours. The parade at two a.m. always includes an ambulance, a firetruck, a police cruiser, and a rescue vehicle, all with sirens sounding and lights spinning. Occasionally, the four vehicles left in silence, sometimes the ambulance screeched away in the direction of one of the hospitals, and infrequently, but occasionally, a nosy neighbor might espy the gurney leave one of the three buildings with one large black bag – and it was not filled with autumn leaves.

One-hundred years before hereabouts farmers worried about which cow to present at an annual agricultural fair. There might be some discussion about a trip into the city if only so much time need not be sacrificed for the trip. And what might one expect anyway after the hours and the effort. No, the reward, if there was any, just wasn't worth it. One had to consider that cow and the trip down the hillside, right through the creek (no narrow bridges then), and into the village for a roast on the green and some sparse few other activities. No lights, no sirens. And no rescue needed. None available.

True, an inordinate amount of time we spent worrying about our after-life. The Reverend in the little gothic Baptist chapel provided proverbs of concern and not of acceptance or reconciliation. He congratulated every farmer on the weight of their cows and he drank heartily of their milk.

Yes, times were different, but changing too. Along the river – not more than a stone's throw from the chapel – Bob Ewell started the wireworks.

Meanwhile, the Roger-Smith boy had taken an inordinate liking to the cow. He had seen it at the fair and it was all we could do to calm the lad to have him up the hill to see to all the chores so related to its care and feeding. The lad glowed it seemed during these visits. There would be no stopping him, though, from the life he'd later choose despite our warnings.

On our last trip to the city, one member of our group fell behind the others, hurried so to catchup, but then became separated from the rest by a large delivery van unloading its wares. By then the day had darkened and he hurried down a parallel avenue hoping to rejoin us and yet soon the street narrowed. He came upon a large church in collegiate style and greeted a solitary priest who stood out front. He said, "Good evening, Father." And the priest said, "Bless you" and then our friend came to a high solid wall of stone, higher than he could climb, but noted a slim alley between church and wall leading in the direction he assumed would soon return him to our company. The narrow walk had no light, and he could only wonder if it indeed offered passage to the other street.

We had to call an ambulance last night for Mr. Ernst Paine, the former professor of philosophy at the College of Saint John. We had no doubt where he'd be going: first, to Saint Mary's Hospital and then to his grave. The lights swirled about the neighborhood and sirens sounded louder than ever, especially on account of the ungodly hour.

The next day protestors marched up the street to the governor's residence and made their demands. They asked for restrictions regarding the coming and going of emergency vehicles of all sorts. They might as well have asked the governor to intercede on everyone's behalf regarding death and dying. Such, however, remains far removed from his purview. The governor neither heard nor saw those protestors. He was not at home that day, but in Fairfield visiting the sick.

We had saved the blue one. The green one became a tree. All of this because of sliding rugs on polished floors or strange spots on forearms. Some of us knew better than to count on rescue. We were content to pay taxes, make charitable contributions, and claim deductions for as long as possible. Our boats, ready in the closet: we would not be stopped.

Upon his arrival they had asked Ernst – mind, body, spirit. Embarrassed he had to admit. Mind, no. No mind. Then he added but body, yes; yes, body. He paused for a few moments of thought and then at last he stated and spirit too. Certainly spirit.

Dr. Ridenour found Ernst's thinking confused, told him so, and put him to bed. We'll try again tomorrow, Dr. Ridenour said. And when morning came, there he stood ready to ask Ernst once again – mind, body, spirit. This is what you get, Ernst thought, for choosing the correct cow and keeping outside the city gate. Jeffers noted, "At night he remembers freedom / And flies in a dream, the dawn ruins it."

I didn't send everybody home just so we could feed some fair-trade child. Better someone take care of the cows and the tractor, too. Change the oil. That task first and then maybe feed the others. Enough of this dream of the prize cow. Let's bale hay.

No time for dancing. No time for the stars to come out, the full moon, or the blue lake. I told them – you can't know what they'll find once inside. Like going to the storage shed for a Coke and then finding it all gone, empty. That's what I said but they weren't listening or all those vehicles together made too much noise. No wonder no one slept at night. No wonder. And then in day there were all the exercises to be done. Hours of them. In the swimming pool and out on the roads, better in – aging joints protected. The elevator walls protected by plush pads, a sign of careful management. Manage the body, the farm, the neighbor. And a new fire alarm system too and yet still those leaks and those late-night lights and sirens. Our reputation has deteriorated. I hope something good will emerge from this darkness, the advertisements say. Begin here: the first step; the second will follow one behind. Nothing to compare, nothing else. Though some of us prefer to reach for the stars.

Up the steps and through the door. They know the routine by now. Well-practiced and precise, they are lifesavers often and they'll save one tonight. But it is so confusing: mine, yours, or someone else's? Maybe the professor's? There's a gathering protest outside. A storm, a gathering storm, as they say. Here are more police. Here comes Engine One. The board chairman turns on the lights by the pool; the clock, stolen.

Situated mid-block there are two near equal-distant options for departure: turn north or turn south. In the latter direction a vehicle passes large homes on both sides of the street before making a left-hand turn that takes one down a commercial stretch with a gas station or two, a coffee-shop, and taco take-out storefront, a used clothes store, a few law offices, one funeral home, and a package store. Then at a traffic light turn left again and pass two churches, a number of high-rise apartment towers, a near-vacant office building, one remaining gothic estate in bad repair, and a local TV station. Go straight at the light and enter the gates.

Or exit to the north, proceed a short distance pass several large homes, two churches, and a park entrance, and then turn right. Go down a slight hill pass some more large houses, including one that leaves holiday decorations out most of the year, go beyond the Historical Society, two gated enclaves, and the old women's college, up a slight incline to the light, turn left and immediately there you are and so no matter which route you choose you end up at the same destination. One route has an extra light and one has no place to stop for food or gas.

III

Religious Studies

We put our hands in clay and then we lifted our hands from the clay. Now we had four hands each – those attached at our wrists to our arms and those on the table before us. We were able to take the latter hands home later that day, to carry them home and to say, "Look Mom; look Dad. Look at what I made. Look at what I made today." And another day, another set of hands: these framed and on a wall one hand down and one hand up; both surrounded by colorful dots; both accurate and life-like but rendered abstract by their placement on a blue-colored field; both isolated from whatever body held these hands -- palms up, as if in greeting. The framed hands led me to search for those clay hands. I looked in a box that contained old photos and clippings, thinking that they might be at the bottom of it. They were not, but there was a blue bell that once hung over a crib, a bell with a short string: pull it and the bell rings *Jesus loves me Yes, I know*, a lesson long forgotten or lost.

A New Day

That night it was the stars not Smith or Providence: an opinion. In regarding the exterior surface, substitute an image (bought for a song and sold for a requiem). In regarding the exterior surface – meaning otherwise absent. Called Off Cancels Tour. In regarding the exterior surface, every time an avocado, more contradiction than confluence – infighting left wreckage and not the intimacy of insurance. And then not a chicken in every pot, but a song in every heart; a vigorous hymn to the inevitable right now. Slammed with negotiations, cold ground, twist and turn and drill down. One will look down. Greet them. Open the black case, all exterior glow. Small observations make and then what happens, happens – a brief illusion of renewal. When you open the back, promises become something one plays, a universe of sound that turns out necks and frets and tuning keys. One holds an axe and then twists and turns and breaks free. The bow looked best and so very young, the bouquet at the office. Substitution repaid the exterior. Sans, again, the cola day here. First the feet then the brains. Being pirates again -- all those faces renounce, choose, make. In a pew -- they return talking of the exterior.

The Old Psalm Tune

At the office we were asked: cremation or burial? I hid my bandaged hand, burned already by an oven. I wondered, does the mind remain cognizant, do eyes look out and see the attendant mourners, and does one cross over, and then will I see Fess Parker but wish for mother?

The Cone of Uncertainty

I've been nothing but worry with traveling these days. That's right, me – who has never been anywhere. It's been more than a year since we've seen the Sunday supplement travel section and now, we have inside open again; the red-wing black-bird has come back to the same spot as last year and the one before and the one before that. She sings, better a bench than a person, something that allows sit as well as sight. When gusts come, leaves return – or towers; birds' rising whistles and those stems that snap back into place, a positivity praised as a precious beacon of hope.

Fortunes

Tell the truth about the bloodworm's chances to survive. Tell the horse all about its clumsy dance partner who lives very happily inside an enlarged intestine and the copperhead who slithers on the floor frightening old horses to the very end of their tether, to the very rear of their cage. Tell the poor creatures not to worry about who it is that crawls about in the dark cavern to avoid a fisherman's rusted hook, a trout's sharp teeth, while the poor host kicks at the dirt and repeats it last meal. Tell the cautious fisherman the story about the one who ran into the lake chased by a snake that rolled over the water like a magic wheel from one side to the other. Tell the truth about hoop snakes and copperheads to all the children who need to be warned and to all the fishermen who don't believe in magic, to all the wives alone now that the snake has come. Tell me how to fend for myself in the dark, how to stay out of the lake, out of the horse's midsection. Who has the talisman that can protect the innocent? Who has the wafer that can redeem the fallen? Tell the truth about the bloodworm's chances. Tell the truth about mine. I can take it.

Should I tell Hong he got the prize? I'd have to slow down. My impulse had been to choose Kevin, but I know he'll be back. And there's that young person with the odd routine: a half-mile jog – maybe – and then right here on the track such a strange series of calisthenics. But she seems quite fit. If my routine were that brief, I wouldn't bother. Too much effort to change and change again. I do not know why these five miles are so difficult today. Maybe the young mistress of stretches and lunges has passed her cold on to me. It seems hard to breathe. There must be an explanation.

The bronze age will begin in the morning, a morning that makes faces visible to words: dry words, dead words. Rain falls with bits of the sky. Such weather appears like disaster: too many questions begged. Yet, something after so many drops.

At the start of the study, I made sure to read the New Testament. This was not an old heirloom, but the copy purchased at the college bookstore for Rev. Fritz Shafer's Bible class. Old enough, this copy, now. And I wrote in notebooks so many aphoristic quotable phrases. Where are they now?

The next day a trans-esophageal exam, a pelican too grim perhaps for salvation and problems that were without dollars a matter of timing. The cloud elongated as more members joined the team. I received an injection of Atropine and chewed some children's aspirin.

"Los Angeles weather," Joan Didion wrote, "is the weather of catastrophe, of apocalypse, and, just as the reliably long and bitter winters of New England determine the way life is lived there, so the violence and the unpredictability of the Santa Ana affect the entire quality of life in Los Angeles, accentuate its impermanence, its unreliability. The wind shows us how close to the edge we are."

Walls shaken by the first undulating movement were at once overthrown. I waited – prostrate – in a small room in the emergency wing from mid-afternoon to mid-evening. Yet, there remained the question of timing. Strength and stamina, yes; courage, no – a balance between competing claims of complexity and generality: a floating piece of the tumor. This terminology is well accepted – ischemic, cerebellar, and vertebral.

Non si sa dove si vada e pur si parte. For what is the life of a poet but a moon harvest? Wherein we are called, therein we do abide.

After I woke up, a nurse and a doctor checked on me. Schools spent $11.7 billion on intercollegiate sports, almost twice what they brought in that year. The light, the quiet, and the sound of birds. And after the seventh week, I looked at the scar. We know, to some extent, our interior psyche; the inside of our bodies, almost not at all. July 31 – sore back; heart rate: 63. A simple thing that does so much, the great cut.

"So neither the one who plants nor the one who waters is anything, but only God who gives the growth." 1 Corinthians 3:7 (Yes, but what about he who cuts? "They shall run and not be weary … " Isaiah 40:31. May 7 – heartrate 52, blood pressure 114 / 60.)

In the words of John Hollander:

> thou, whitestap, lurching through
> The high-grown brush; thou, pliant-footed
> Implex; thou, awagabu.

A century and one-half before James Abraham Hillhouse, who lived where so often John Hollander would later walk, warned that "but every precept which has been given will be ineffectual in forming the mind of the poet unless, aloof from the world, much of his time be passed in solitude and reflection." Thou must study "the Book of Nature, which Providence has Spread."

Only one turtle egg in 1,445. "Ideally," Sarris thought, "the strongest personality should be the director" (an old retired ravioli manufacturer from Long Island City). What is the inference to be drawn from these facts? "The writer, after writing," Italo Calvino wrote in 1964, "finds that he is the poorest of men."

It is done. There is no reason to repeat the catastrophe of this year. We know, to some extent, our interior psyche; the insides of our bodies not at all. Some doctors say to eat cheese in moderation.

The next day a trans-esophageal exam revealed at least one tumor. At that time my pulse rate dropped to the mid-thirties. At 9:30, I moved to a room. Even the dogs eat the crumbs that fall from their master's table. Matthew 15:27.

He who endures to the end will be saved. Mark 13:13. Words are like numbers; sometimes they add-up and other times they lessen: dispatches from the front of the yet-to-be. History begins simultaneously in language and in mystery. I do not think celebration the appropriate word.

It is the gap I fell into, the "romantic tenements of rose and ice" (Stevens). I might have been alone even if others were present. I could have said hello or goodbye.

I still see them some nights and that troubles me. What are they asking? If we could walk again to where something might be purchased – the department of departed ones. They haunt me or hurry me to where the wakeful attend. What is it that parents ask? You too my son, they seem to say, can do something good if not miraculous. Yet the boy who walks does not fly.

Coumadin – six months exact. Let eye-doctor know of spontaneous dissection. Stone Street near Wall Street. Non so dove sono. Non so dove siamo. "Every good poem," Daniel Hoffman told us, "is built on the bones of one-hundred failures." Nothing bad can happy to you. (Frost – "Nothing Gold Can Stay.")

If you're healthy and have a bit of ill-health, you'll be much better off than if you are unhealthy and have a bit of ill-health. "And we run because we like it / Through the broad bright land" (Charles Sorley). Runners cross the start line at last year's race. Not this year.

"Hear" heart and "feel" heart at night at the back of the neck and feel as if had felt the same feeling before. "Long is the way / And hard, that out of Hell leads up to Light." Milton – "Freely they stood who stood, and fell who fell."

May 20th – home; May 21st – some short walks.

"To have a mind full of peace merely fill it full of peace. It's as simple as that." Rev. Norman Vincent Peale.

It does not suffice. But it is indispensable.

According to Howells, "They pronounced that the children would be taught certain branches of learning, and that the whole Bible would be placed in their hands, to be studied and understood." Later at the age of sixty-four he "pruned" such lines and, as he said, "with a free hand ... "

"Blessed are you when men revile you and persecute you and utter all kinds of evil against you falsely on my account." So said Jesus: Matthew 5:11. Persecution versus acceptance and toleration: A Protestant monument in the town cemetery. The palazzo restored and now a wedding reception banquet hall. – "that your joy may be full" (John 15:11).

A kind of stroke and a faulty valve. A half-marathon, sluggish the whole way. (Sentences so bound together that to read them one enters a state of reverie.)

And now what? Blepharitis. Swaying – a windblown sign, an arrow pointed at red bricks and betraying an original idea or become a stop sign or a dead-end sign, something that dictates, shouts, commands, and steals. Until daylight, the accident of local circumstances dethroned our memory of former days. When the film finished, only a handful clapped and sporadically, as if an obligation. Stevens put it his way: "The plum survives it poems."

The vacuum taken and the key. Now high up in the light while below another has his drag, his smoke. Variety improved with another type of questionnaire. Dr. Taylor had no trained pastors, no church buildings, little money, no literature, and strong opposition. (Unacknowledged and sojourning for a while in America.)

Park the car in the far lot for "Thou shall neither vex a stranger, nor oppress him" (Exodus 22:21). And Ezra Pound, the poet, later planted syrup-producing American maples near Brunnenburg Castle, but only managed to introduce poison ivy to the region.

Resolved. That we express our hearty appreciation to the brethren and sisters of Shiloh Church for their generous hospitality and cordiality. 1918.

Resolved. Not any song will do. Not the notes contained, boxed, nor the longest solo. Nor the final bow. These people have natures that will respond like a violin under the bow; they reverence poetry and art and are sensitive to thoughts of beauty.

Gia fatto. Prima di continuare, vorrei invitarvi a fare delle domande. Some exercises in the hotel. October 20th – slept late. Short walk to Chiesa Valdese. Dinner at Il Pizzicotto in neighborhood. In *The Shape of Content*, Ben Shahn said "form is an instrument, not a tyrant."

"Scrittore," Erri De Luca asked of us, "piante un albero per ogni nuovo libro." But on the 21st, slept late dreaming of the Bible as an instrument of liberty and democracy and not of tyranny and war. Prossima volta. "The light shines in the darkness, and the darkness has not overcome it." John 1:5.

Ran three miles on a treadmill at the hotel. Embroidered stories. Drove over the Bear Mountain Bridge. Walked down Pine and up South. On way in from airport the President's cavalcade drove by our taxi. A long wait for our bags. Ads from design magazines with Mexican workers painted into them. "The scaffolds are not safe, for the rich must ever profit more." Pietro di Donato.

Sandwiches from Mariano's across the street. The state of painting such that the subjects can scarcely be made out. Back to the hotel. A North African city made out of couscous. "Flesh," George Herbert thought, "is but the glass which holds the dust that measures all our time." Send message: air traffic controllers' strike in France. Got back near on time, but no luggage. At a castle, we saw some art and musical instruments and then walked through the park.

Enrico Caruso purchased a large picture of a sunset. It was painted in Glastonbury, Connecticut. Words are stones: work hard to find the right one. Sunrise. The limitations of an afternoon.

Jade is a stone; granite, an eye: size of a softball, flat as a pancake. The rotation of stars, the flux of tides, the water – the solidity of it. Speak of the flame / stone: polar ice.

March 11th – pizza pie and birthday cake. Fluid retention. Fluid removed. Eight weeks of taking weight each morning and noting its small fluctuations in a notebook. Exercise stopped again and started again, too. April 10th – first Fisher Meadow run after five weeks – six miles.

"Keep America as it was," so Gino Speranza said in 1925. He will look at his hands and feet and he will not recognize them.

The walls of a cavern, once entered may collapse upon the novice. What might be pulled from the wreckage? There is no change, only the repetition of rote behaviors. Others insist that they will not pay for that which will never pay and yet each week they return to the lottery.

"Naples's streets," Erri De Luca said, "are flow regulated by crisis." H. Tarr Photography, 960 Flatbush Avenue, Brooklyn.

One day he saw on my bedside table a Protestant edition of the Bible, and he started back in horror, as if it were a serpent. "Such books as you read, Doctor. Throw it away, I beg of you!" Carlo Levi.

Professor Pretzel's ideas are so twisted that I take them with a grain of salt.

Two preparations beginning in the afternoon. Up all night. Went in, woke up a few hours later. Great discomfort at night. Slept sitting up.

April, 1955. "I am going to the hospital today or tomorrow: St. Francis, and at best will be there for about three weeks. No visitors. After that, I ought to be in good shape for the next twenty or thirty years." Wallace Stevens (October 2, 1879 – August 2, 1955)

Rather than a frame for a story, consider the limitations of framing a life. End with a grand metaphysical speculation situated in the most ordinary of things. Mystery creates a frame as its only explanation. Consider the hotels actors occupy.

I did not think about my shoes and yet I feel them and the feeling is not unpleasant. It is the knee, the right one, that pings when moved. The fact of this discomfort cannot be denied. I have no words at my disposal sufficient to describe the soreness. I need a crystal ball that makes no forecast but puts an end to a present ache.

Run, I will carry you and I will lead you home, and there I will carry you. Isaiah 46:4.

One surged ahead and another said let's stay with him. They had a fast pace across the causeway. They crossed a river and swam for the water rose above their heads. They held ropes and kept moving. Maybe one of them won. The water had been that cold.

I slowed the vehicle and looked closely and saw that those were my parts, my body parts, and not parts from the Bonneville. Saint Augustine wrote, "I turned my thoughts into myself and said, 'Who are you?' And I answered, 'A human being.'"

It must have been the Spinelli come at night to ruin this day. Lorenzo went over to where Enzo slept and found him still asleep. He kicked Enzo who groaned, "Go away. Go away."

Enzo gave a package to his sister and told her to bury it out by the oat field. His sister felt its weight in her hands and asked what was in it. The head of our employer, Enzo replied. His sister said you must be kidding me. And he said, okay. It's a pumpkin that's gone bad. Now go and bury it like I said.

The water becomes concrete: red letters and blue stains navigate fog and stone traps. Steel edges rise to the surface. A foreman parks his truck and looks for us. He spits a patch of yellow, no work for his idle hands. Then Peter came to Jesus and asked, "Lord, how many times shall I forgive my brother?" (Matthew 18:21)

Twist and turn and drill down for observation, a brief illusion of renewal; a universe of sound. "Health and salvation can only be found in motion," so wrote Soren Kierkegaard. A brief illusion of renewal.

Would James Merrill have put away the tea cup? How old would he have turned this year! Think of all he might have added had these additional years been granted: more news from islands; from friends about pets and cocktails and the past. After I heard him that time at Bard College, did he leave for Greece, Stonington, or a hospital? "The page you scrawled / Turns. A new day. Fresh snow."

We cannot but speak the things which we have seen and heard. Acts 4:20.

Church parking only. Violators will be persecuted.

Outside town a factory hums all day turning out necks and frets and tuning keys. On the way home, workers whistle. I would like to serenade you, but I am out of tune, out of touch and yet still in love, a universe of sound.

Stories, Michel de Certeau said, "are composed with the world's debris." I remember anisette cookies. I see yellow flowers in a pot on the center of the table.

Someone holds a box, stands still by a box turned upside-down and two other people walk by beneath an open umbrella.

The key to cooking sloppy Joe's is using a potato masher to break up the beef.

I'm sure we saved the blue one. The green one became a tree.

"the husk of longing tends toward a dwelling-place" – Richard Deming

wandervogel – climb into the word

Dad always said skin a fish; get a bone. What he meant by that was those fish that come in close to shore, those fish you can catch by the bucketful for a few days each spring seem great – a blessing even – but how easy to choke on all those abundant bones in all those skinny bottom-dwellers! And that's how he felt about life. Anything that came in by the bucketful best be tossed out.

And mom said something all the time, too. Just the other night I dreamt those words but when I woke, I could not recall them. My mother, head of the Sunday school, and I so liked the bright colored illustrations of Jesus in the garden or walking on water.

"In spring the earth sings as if it knew love songs by heart while a sense of loss still pervades poetry past and present oh what is it in us that prefers singing of loss instead of present ecstasies" – Lawrence Ferlinghetti, *Little Boy*.

Exodus out of Brooklyn. Organize by date. If same year, alphabetical by building name. Oh John Clare, you "self-consumer" woe. Scrambled eggs, and then one has a tooth removed and unexpected stitches. The leaves toss upside-down as one descends downstairs to walk in the park. More maps and statistics; little note of what songs. A roll-bar and a spoiler: everyone needs them. A mix of mindlessness and monitoring: there had been other productions. One of them was Canadian: minutiae of military operations.

Moses will not sue. Ears of discernment will grow a list. The leaves turn upside-down as I descend the stairs to talk to you. Fresh baked bread in hand, an offering and a comfort. Glorified to see the Lord in our welcome. We have oxygen in the air. We have fertile soil.

Anton Steenwijk attends medical school and finds the perfect career for one who has suffered trauma: he becomes an anesthesiologist.

Regrets

All clubs and parties are renounced. We seldom leave the house. The old bricks often bear the prints of fingers that shaped them. We had a small situation this a.m. with our coffee pot but it is fine. The sound of the wind through a mask – an open mouth.

Invariably we return to our home. We leave on a strong tide and come back in a cold drizzle. The harbor lights shine bright against the gray cliffs. Our flag flies high and we wave and shout hello and by golly we feel wonderful. But then the thought strikes: these waters, brisk and salty, a cramp – a side-stitch or the sting of an eel or a sudden shift in tides. Westward we sailed and as we did so, we became still and sullen. Yet, I recall the time we sat in ropes class laughing at the terrible mess we had made of our assignment and how the instructor chastised us after the class had ended. A boat had run aground, one that no one knew had so many holes in it. One soul had been briefly framed in a stateroom window. The wind bit at the glass. We saw backpacks crisscrossed with cord move up the coast toward the cliffs. Tied together for safety, there a gap in the blue.

The Gift

Alice wanted to recline in the sun but since she wrenched her neck earlier that week, she first pushed some sand into a mound upon which to rest her head. In the early morning light this heap of sand had a reddish tint that picked-up the color of her two-piece suit. "This will do very nicely, indeed," she said to air and water and breeze for there was no one to hear her at such an early hour, not a surfer or fisherman. She reclined and sighed deeply, "Ah," and just then as she stretched out on her terry beach towel her right foot hit a hard surface. She grabbed her foot and saw that her pedicure had been ruined and she determined to discover this awful object and hurl it through space into the deep of the sea. She leaned forward, grabbed it, brought it toward her face, and contemplated it. The orb-like object had a milky translucence and within it there appeared a separate and different object, suspended – perhaps a moon rock, she thought. She found it impossible to hurl this artifact ocean-ward and instead turned it in her hands and contemplated it some more. Then the pincers of a sand-crab struck her left foot and Alice reacted in lightning speed, smashed the creature to a pancake with her moon-rock orb. She then pulled her phone from her bag, called Nail-Pro and made an appointment for a new pedicure that afternoon. Then she eased back down – slowly because of her sore neck – rested her head on the pillow of sand, her moon-rock orb her only company.

Origins

Suppose a knot of blue and silver glass, twisted and tense, occupies some sunlit shelf. The green of a vase may swirl skyward and the nut-tray's color holds only so much of that one tone and none of that translatable shape. Far from our sky-colored shelf, factory workers punch out scores and scores of such sacred beginnings as this one. Even so, the philosopher of paradise dreams that his world braces for dawn.

Muse Me Thus

And everything has to start: blue water in the oceans, for example; or clouds above green fields and dust along the edges of that carpet; that too, and endless charts that correct error and a fragrance that perpetuates gospel hours. All of it. Ghostlike, we are the batteries that hammer our steel in the shadow of an abandoned factory. Jagged rocks make our walk tiresome until some kindly tractor pulls up sometime around late next century. My, my, what had the soothsayer said when nobody answered even after three rings of the telephone? On the chalkboard, a message – perhaps the words of a prophet? –silence followed: restless clouds circled above. These were signs that something might have happened. Then we looked up a word in the dictionary, up in the thesaurus, a word very much like the speakers at a festival shout-out while those gathered, hear nothing at all.

This Reminds Me

We drove to Brooklyn to talk about the project and ate sandwiches at a deli. There was a giant hole in the ground with steam gushing out of it and I wondered what they might find down there. Another class made a similar trip and I wrote something about pool sharks even though the sign said "rectory." I tried to clean out John's basement apartment and there were many colorful paintings he had done and I didn't even know he had ever painted. I drove through the tunnel after a funeral and thought it might fill up with water and we would not be able to get out. We went to a diner in Philadelphia and the two guys next to us ordered club sandwiches. We took a tour of the palace in Amsterdam and saw the giant Atlas sculpture with the planet on his back. We heard a lecture in Blithewood and then walked outside where snow fell through pine trees. Around Christmas mother taped cards into the glass squares of the French doors. In graduate school we went to the Rittenhouse Library to see *Gone with the Wind* and couldn't understand why so many people like it so much and still can't. I sat in the library and fell asleep and you noticed. I do remember what I was reading. We drove into Brooklyn for dinner and I got a present, though I can't recall what I got and come to think of it maybe we took the bus and train. I caught fish for the first time. I think we ate them, but they had too many bones and too little taste. I went camping in New Hampshire with my brother. I thought he carried much that was unnecessary, but I don't think the unneeded weight slowed us down. One time I walked over here and wrote about an ancestor. Men with thick, long beards remind me of people I never met and a time I will never understand.

Reunion

I want to know more than I know. If feeling better, I could be there at noon. And then: I see you reading a book. What is it to know? Here are the words in black and white. But I don't know how they are understood by you. Return to your book. A light comes on. I want to know more than I know.

Uneven Surface

Keep your ethnic war-cry. Your name may be garbled, attacked by neighbors. Strike your sensible arrangement and start your wheeling, your jumping, and your eagerness. Horses and a favorite. Houses and so on. Oh muse, no matter how you cut it, it's going to be sliced.

Legends

The three caravels were two, the Santa Maria belonged to the class we call "carack." Sancho Panza was not a fat slob; stocky, he suffered an inexhaustible appetite, habitual but nothing extraordinary. Joseph was a boy when he married Mary – none of the disciples wrote that he was an old guy. And Samson was no dumb jock that could not communicate with Delilah and hence was shorn; those two were in love more than Romeo and Juliette. Time is not ash under the lava that covers Pompeii and hides facts, time is a fissure. Now restore legends.

After Erri De Luca

Letter Home

I know you'd like it here: the park, the Duomo, the restaurants, the high fashion. True: it feels so much larger than Rome and more international: too many bankers and diplomats. Yet when the soloist struck the notes of Paganini all criticism evaporated in the sonority of the concert hall. I wish you could have heard it – played on a period instrument made in the sixteenth-century in nearby Cremona. And then we were off to the trattoria that the journalist had recommended. Late, true, for residents of Connecticut but the wines of Piedmont and Umbria soon revived us. And now I sit here in the breakfast room – *sala colazione* – and write to you this simple message – espresso in hand.

Blue

His shirt is blue. His tie is blue. His sweater is blue. There is even a trace of blue along the edge of his eyeglass frames. But he seems to blush a bit in the presence of the camera and the cameraman. Or is it that the cameraman's lights cast a rosy hue across the subject's face? The cameraman has failed to force this subject to smile. Perhaps the subject regrets having this photo taken, this portrait created or has his mind wandered elsewhere – thinking of things to be done, lines to be written, words to be spoken – and dinner too? He is hungry now and in his eyes off somewhere in the distance is a leg of lamb.

Joys of the Walk Sign

One note affixed to what he thinks might be a charm, an overabundance of an idea or a sound. What the townspeople sought; what they still seek – before the leaves fall. He spits into his hands, claps his hands to begin what's to be done this day like a moon rising in the bottom of his shoe. He pushes his hands into clay from the chaos of the sea. Last night he wiggled. He spun dervish-like. The geography of the town circumscribes the possible. One looks skyward, a visionary, and another looks downward and greets no one. He tries to rationalize that odd feeling of being surrounded by those who would harm him and how he lashes out at them. Perhaps they are his neighbors. He commits himself to adding his name and number to all directories.

Her name might be Alice. She always carries an umbrella. The sun succumbs to clouds. Folded tissues and used ones balled up into a corner of this bag bought from a street vendor some time ago. Enough coin to fill the parking meters of a small city – say Poughkeepsie. A wallet within the bag almost bursts its dual clasps. Cards for various memberships date back a decade and more, and a register accompanies a leather-clad checkbook. There are photographs of family and a tattered love note penned one February. There are medications for headaches and arthritis, sunburn and snake-bite.

She buys a carton of cigarettes, steps outside, and then she goes back into the store for matches. The store attendant tells her she must buy something to get matches. She says nothing, but holds up the carton. Right, he says, and passes a pack of matches across the counter. Outside it starts to rain. She cups her hands, but either the wind blows out a match or the rain puts it out. At the cemetery she sits by the largest monument – its front legs have been knocked out and the chipped slab leans into muddy earth. Some verses, now unreadable, cover the surface; warn of sin or celebrate virtue. She leans against part of the slab; uses it to shield her match and light her cigarette. She inhales and exhales, relaxed by familiarity. She hears a voice, but sees no one. The wind makes a sound like speech and she tries to decipher the words.

IV

Coda: Untitled

First, a map of
Jones Mountain – folded,
but dry; few details;
then the travels
commenced and completed
by an evangelist: an
invitation misplaced,
more maps and statistics,
very little recorded of
the songs they sang.

A folder misplaced, a
scholarship unclaimed.
Red markings too many
and time then to render
red another color. Try
this poet, a labor
organizer. How many
trees out a window?
A new century, a plea
for humility.

I did and don't regret
it: "broad Herculean shoulders"
and "crimson murmurings."
Then: dead birds
on the state highway
followed by a lyric
entitled "Ambition."
Empty. An essay. A
note in May 2020.
Check the video.

The archives are currently
closed, a few future items –
gifted by another; then locked,
not located. Useful?
Pacific and corner of Canal
and some don't request
a reminder; others, grow thinner.
No questionnaire, an exam:
the results, disposed. Things
look excellent, terrific
(Symptoms of NTM infection include)
Please Pay This Amount

Vienna 1906; Now and at
the Hour – Molise, Campania,
Puglia, Basilicata, Calabria –
the necessary calculations
made: Hollywood version,
another story and its eyes
in order, wishing you well
and that you read the handwriting
another version as case in
point for all citizens.

Considered: mission reports
and gifts – "Shiloh Strong."
Description: 5 blueprints
for the house. (The building
of the house was to be like
a day.) He imparted courage
and enthusiasm, a genuine
missionary fervor. And
then the man with bushy hair
and a flower in his hands

held near his lips and
in front of a favored sweater.
And their families invite
you – convention held in
Waterbury. Who is,
Carmela Fiumara?
Oh, our lord and savior,
the print is too small to
read. One succumbs;
another, introduces.
Mrs. Howard, Oxford, Dies.

Reprint or Publication Not
Authorized
By the blessing of God this
station continues
1901 – Springfield
A tear in the envelope
This we will keep
Municipio
According to our records
Nancy Morrell,
Town Clerk

Then more pictures
lots of them
photocopies, not originals
too hard to discard
duplicates even, clipped
seems less the record
the prayer in memory of
offered thanks very much
I finally received the box
I was waiting for
Below is a very brief
biographical sketch

Thank you for the material you sent
Thank you for your reply
Thanks a lot for writing
I think you have done a beautiful job
I perused the report
I am the Resurrection
Authorization for
landscaped walks in place of
streets

And I just got off the phone
primary progress report
guitar studio
borough of
sleep of reason
chokes on the bones
of flat fish
it may have been quixotic
in any light, and in the distance

Juniper Street Mama
Angelina

The Netherlands Shoe Museum
A bridge over the Ramapo without planks
A ride to the Deserted Village
The fireplace in a Taos B & B
Mr. Buzzi
Dan Isaac
Marina Del Ray
Scary alligators
A bear in a tree

Juniper Street Mama
Angelina

Dennis Barone is the author of many books of fiction, poetry, and literary studies. Blaze VOX published his book *On the Bus: Selected Stories* in 2012 and his volume of poetry *Frame Narrative* in 2018. Other works include *Beyond Memory: Italian Protestants in Italy and America* (SUNY Press) and *Sound / Hammer* (Quale Press). He has edited volumes such as *Garnet Poems: An Anthology of Connecticut Poetry Since 1776* (Wesleyan University Press) and *New Hungers for Old: One-Hundred Years of Italian-American Poetry* (Star Cloud Press). He is Professor Emeritus at the University of Saint Joseph, and currently serves as the Poetry Editor for the *Wallace Stevens Journal* and as President of the Hartford Friends and Enemies of Wallace Stevens.

Made in the USA
Middletown, DE
12 January 2022

57704421R10073